A DEMONSTRATION
HANDBOOK
FOR PHYSICS

G. D. FREIER
F. J. ANDERSON

First edition, 1972

Second edition, 1981

Printed in the United States of America

Published by
American Association of Physics Teachers
Publications Department
5112 Berwyn Road
College Park, MD 20740, U.S.A.

ISBN # 0-917853-32-6

PREFACE

This book is presented as a handbook for high school and college teachers who want to demonstrate the phenomena of physics to their classes. Both high school and college teachers should find the experiments to be helpful in showing students how one isolates various phenomena. The demonstrations described in this book are in no way intended to be considered as applications of physics. Instead, these demonstrations of isolated phenomena should serve as building blocks to be fitted together and thus construct real applications which may already be invented or may yet be invented in the future. Conversely, the operations of complex systems may be analyzed in terms of many isolated physical phenomena, providing a better picture of how the complex system works.

Our desire is to have teachers bring to students real physical happenings rather than mathematical models. Many students, especially those destined to become laymen as far as the physical sciences are concerned, can comprehend concepts in terms of physical models much more readily than they can comprehend these same concepts in the form of mathematical models. We also believe that students, who can work well with mathematical models, will have an enriched training if they can visualize better physical models as they carry out their mathematical analyses. Our teaching experience indicates that students are pleased to see demonstrations of the topics we discuss in class, even in more advanced courses.

No attempt has been made to label experiments as high school or college level. This can be done by the teacher, who will often find classes of students carrying out high school level thinking about physics while in college, and, on the other hand, there are special high school classes doing college level thinking in high school. Probably no experiment is too simple. A simple experiment may have an almost correct simple explanation, but it will sometimes require a sophisticated analysis to complete the entire description of the phenomenon.

The perspective drawings for each experiment are intended to be mostly suggestive to the teacher so that he may modify some of the equipment which he has available, and then proceed with a demonstration which in many cases may be better and more meaningful than the one described. If the teacher prepares his lectures or lessons away from the classroom, say at home, the handbook can remind him of what may be available back at the school.

A few of the demonstrations have been invented by the authors, but most of them have been invented by other teachers. Unfortunately, for the purpose of acknowledgement, most of the ideas are old and it is an impossible task to credit the demonstrations to the inventor. It seems that in the area of teaching, the inventor of a teaching method tends to remain anonyomous. This is one of the prices paid by teachers in their struggle to help others.

Many of the experiments are described in more detail in the book entitled Physics Demonstration Experiments, edited by H. Meiners and published by Ronald Press. Many more experiments are found in the book Demonstration Experiments in Physics by R. Sutton and published by McGraw-Hill Company. There are many editions of the German book Einführung in die Physik, written by R. W. Pohl and published by J. Springer which contain a great number of well described demonstration experiments. Those who use this handbook should also realize that there are many other experiments described in the more complete works listed above. We have simply included those experiments which seem to us to form a reasonable complete sequence for the subject matter of a course in general physics. A more theoretical explanation of many of the handbook demonstrations will be found in the book University Physics, Experiment and Theory by G. Freier and is published by Appleton-Century-Crofts. The spirit in which demonstrations are often done is illustrated by "George" in the magazine, The Physics Teacher.

G. D. Freier
F. J. Anderson

Minneapolis, Minnesota
December, 1971

PREFACE TO THE SECOND EDITION

Since the first edition of this book, many new demonstrations have found their way into the teaching of physics and many more old ones have been rediscovered. These additions, which have come from many sources, have increased the number of demonstrations in this book about thirty five percent. While incorporating these new ideas into the book, the work was reorganized and classified somewhat better by subject matter.

In order to realize this additional work we are indebted to many people, directly and indirectly. We want to thank Bruce Eaton for keeping us in touch with the contributions of the AAPT members and for bringing them to Minnesota. We want to thank Edward Nye and Phillip Johnson for their inventory of many older experiments and the modernization of them for new use. Behind these direct efforts will be the clever innovations of physics teachers throughout the world who make the teaching of physics more enjoyable and allow us to clarify physical concepts for our students. Finally, we want to thank Willard E. Anderson of Honeywell Inc. for guidance in editing. It is difficult to properly assemble a "picture book" such as this which is a collection of the work of so many different people. His help made it possible.

Our hope is that physics teachers at all levels will find the book to be useful for organizing and planning their demonstration lectures in physics.

G. D. Freier
F. J. Anderson

Minneapolis, Minnesota
October, 1980

TABLE OF CONTENTS

MECHANICS

FUNDAMENTAL QUANTITIES
    Ma-1.   Length   M- 3
    Ma-2.   Mass   M- 3
    Ma-3.   Time   M- 3
KINEMATICS
    Mb-1.   Reaction Time   M- 3
    Mb-2.   Adding Displacements   M- 4
    Mb-3.   Displacements   M- 4
    Mb-4.   Cycloidal Motion   M- 4
    Mb-5.   Inversor   M- 4
    Mb-6.   Rotation and Relative Translation   M- 5
    Mb-7.   Differential Motion   M- 5
    Mb-8.   Rotation and Translation   M- 5
    Mb-9.   Distance and Time Intervals   M- 5
    Mb-10.   Average and Instantaneous Velocity   M- 6
    Mb-11.   Uniform and Accelerated Motion   M- 6
    Mb-12.   Time Intervals of Fall   M- 6
    Mb-13.   Uniform Acceleration   M- 7
    Mb-14.   Simultaneous Fall   M- 7
    Mb-15.   Time of Flight   M- 7
    Mb-16.   Monkey and Cannon   M- 8
    Mb-17.   Trajectory Model   M- 8
    Mb-18.   Measurement of "g"   M- 8
    Mb-19.   Water Trajectory   M- 9
    Mb-20.   Blackboard Trajectory   M- 9
    Mb-21.   How Fast Does a Bullet Go?   M- 9
    Mb-22.   Velocity of a Bullet.   M-10
    Mb-23.   Obtaining "g" From a Trajectory   M-10
    Mb-24.   Howitzer and Tunnel   M-11
    Mb-25.   Coriolis Acceleration   M-11
    Mb-26.   Coriolis Acceleration With Water   M-12
    Mb-27.   Coriolis Acceleration on Earth   M-12
    Mb-28.   Accelerated Coordinate System   M-13
    Mb-29.   Central Acceleration   M-13
    Mb-30.   Relative Velocity   M-13
    Mb-31.   Velocity and Central Acceleration   M-14
    Mb-32.   Uniform Motion   M-15
INERTIA OF REST
    Mc-1.   Inertia of Rest   M-16
    Mc-2.   Inertia Balls   M-16
    Mc-3.   Inertia Block   M-16
    Mc-4.   Inertia of Rest   M-17
    Mc-5.   Tightening a Hammer Handle   M-17
FORCE AND ACCELERATION
    Md-1.   Reaction Carts   M-17
    Md-2.   Force, Mass, and Acceleration   M-18
    Md-3.   Magnet Reaction Carts   M-18
    Md-4.   Action and Reaction with Air Carts   M-18
INERTIA OF MOTION
    Me-1.   Persistance of Motion   M-19
    Me-2.   Air Table and Pucks   M-19

WEIGHT
    Mf-1.   Weight of a Mass   M-19
    Mf-2.   Vanishing Weight   M-20
LINEAR MOMENTUM
    Mg-1.   Collision Balls   M-20
    Mg-2.   Conservation of Linear Momentum   M-20
    Mg-3.   Elastic Collisions with Air Carts   M-21
    Mg-4.   Realizing Equal Velocities   M-21
    Mg-5.   Reaction Carts   M-22
ROCKETS
    Mh-1.   Rocket Car   M-23
    Mh-2.   Rocket to the Moon   M-23
    Mh-3.   Water Rocket   M-23
    Mh-4.   Ball Bearing Reaction Cart   M-24
    Mh-5.   Reaction to a Stream of Water   M-24
CONSERVATION OF LINEAR MOMENTUM
    Mi-1.   Velocity of a Softball   M-25
    Mi-2.   Recoil of a Cannon   M-25
    Mi-3.   Ballistic Pendulum   M-26
    Mi-4.   Velocity of Bullet Using the Air Track M-26
COMPONENTS OF FORCE
    Mj-1.   Vector Sum of Forces   M-27
    Mj-2.   Forces on an Inclined Plane   M-27
    Mj-3.   Breaking Wire   M-27
FRICTION
    Mk-1.   Force of Friction   M-27
    Mk-2.   Rolling and Sliding Friction   M-28
    Mk-3.   Brakes on Front and Rear Wheels   M-28
    Mk-4.   Angle of Repose   M-28
TENSION AND PRESSURE FORCES
    Ml-1.   Tension in a String   M-28
    Ml-2.   Bed of Nails   M-29
CENTRAL FORCES
    Mm-1.   Centripetal Force   M-29
    Mm-2.   Centripetal Force   M-29
    Mm-3.   Rolling Chain   M-30
    Mm-4.   Centrifuge   M-30
    Mm-5.   Loop the Loop   M-30
    Mm-6.   Friction and Tipping in Central Acceleration M-31
    Mm-7.   Hand Cranked Centrifuge   M-31
    Mm-8.   Equal Pressure Surface   M-31
GRAVITATION
    Mn-1.   Cavendish Balance   M-32
TORQUES
    Mo-1.   Loaded Beam   M-32
    Mo-2.   Force Disc   M-32
    Mo-3.   Moments   M-32
    Mo-4.   Tipping Block   M-33
    Mo-5.   Grip Bar   M-33
    Mo-6.   Torque Independent of Lever Arm   M-33
    Mo-7.   Loaded Beam   M-33
    Mo-8.   Forces on a Ladder   M-34
    Mo-9.   No Horizontal Force   M-34
CENTER OF MASS AND CENTER OF GRAVITY
    Mp-1.   Center of Mass Motion   M-34
    Mp-2.   Discus with Shifting CM   M-34
    Mp-3.   Disc Rolling Uphill   M-35
    Mp-4.   Balancing Horse   M-35
    Mp-5.   Balancing Two Forks and Match   M-35

Mp-6.	Unicycle	M-36
Mp-7.	Irregular Shape	M-36
Mp-8.	Earth-Moon System	M-36
Mp-9.	Leaning Tower of Pisa	M-36
Mp-10.	Acrobat	M-37
Mp-11.	Shifting Center of Gravity	M-37
Mp-12.	Center of Gravity of a Stool	M-37
Mp-13.	Center of Gravity of a Potato	M-38
Mp-14.	Tipping Block on Incline	M-38
Mp-15.	Weight of a Broom	M-38
Mp-16.	Seesaw Center of Mass	M-39
Mp-17.	Motion of Center of Mass	M-39
Mp-18.	Motion of Center of Mass on Air Table	M-39
Mp-19.	Acceleration of Center of Mass	M-40

STABILITY

Mq-1.	Stability	M-40
Mq-2.	Stability of Cone and Sphere	M-40

EXCHANGE OF POTENTIAL AND KINETIC ENERGY

Mr-1.	Rolling Uphill	M-41
Mr-2.	Conservation of Energy	M-41
Mr-3.	Stopped Pendulum	M-41
Mr-4.	Rolling Spool	M-41
Mr-5.	Angular Motion	M-42
Mr-6.	Large Pendulum	M-42

ROLE OF MOMENT OF INERTIA IN ROTATIONAL MOTION

Ms-1.	Racing Discs	M-42
Ms-2.	Rotational Energy	M-43
Ms-3.	Racing Rotators	M-43
Ms-4.	Moments of Inertia	M-43
Ms-5.	Whirlagig	M-43
Ms-6.	Force Between Surface and Rolling Object	M-44
Ms-7.	Linear and Angular Dynamics	M-44

ANGULAR MOMENTUM

Mt-1.	Angular Momentum	M-45
Mt-2.	Ballet Dancer with Dumbbells	M-45
Mt-3.	Baseball Player	M-45
Mt-4.	Angular Momentum of a Train	M-46
Mt-5.	Buzz Button	M-46
Mt-6.	Lawn Sprinkler	M-46
Mt-7.	Impact Parameter	M-47
Mt-8.	Transfer of Angular Momentum	M-47

TOPS AND GYROSCOPES

Mu-1.	Bicycle Wheel	M-48
Mu-2.	Precession of Gyro	M-48
Mu-3.	Old Fashioned Top	M-48
Mu-4.	Gyro in a Suitcase	M-49
Mu-5.	Spin and Rotation	M-49
Mu-6.	Instantaneous Axis	M-49
Mu-7.	Precessing Top	M-50
Mu-8.	Feel of a Gyroscope	M-50
Mu-9.	Bicycle Effects	M-50
Mu-10.	MITAC Gyroscope	M-51
Mu-11.	Balancing Ladder	M-51
Mu-12.	Air Suspended Gyroscope	M-52
Mu-13.	Maxwell's Gyro	M-53
Mu-14.	Spin Flipping	M-53
Mu-15.	Gyroscope on a Trapeze	M-53
Mu-16.	Monorail Car	M-54
Mu-17.	Tippy-Top	M-54

Mu-18.	Spinning Football	M-54
Mu-19.	Flipping Iron Slug	M-54
Mu-20.	Rotational Stability	M-55
Mu-21.	Spinning Lariat	M-55

WORK AND POWER
Mv-1.	Pile Driver	M-56
Mv-2.	Power	M-56
Mv-3.	Work to Remove Tape	M-56
Mv-4.	Generator and Light Bulb	M-56

LOSS OF ENERGY AND RESTITUTION
Mw-1.	Loss of Energy	M-57
Mw-2.	Falling Stick with Pennies	M-57
Mw-3.	Coefficient of Restitution	M-57
Mw-4.	Collision Time Pendulum	M-58

SIMPLE HARMONIC MOTION
Mx-1.	Simple Harmonic Motion	M-58
Mx-2.	Projection Model of SHM	M-58
Mx-3.	Mass on a Spring	M-59
Mx-4.	Force and Displacement	M-59
Mx-5.	Drunken Sailor	M-59
Mx-6.	Clockspring Pendulum	M-60
Mx-7.	Air Cart Mass and Spring	M-60
Mx-8.	Graphical Display of Mechanical Resonance	M-60
Mx-9.	Damped Pendulum	M-61
Mx-10.	Adjustable Coupled Pendulum	M-61
Mx-11.	Wilburforce Pendulum	M-61
Mx-12.	Coupled Pendulums	M-62
Mx-13.	Resonance Reeds	M-62
Mx-14.	Coupled Oscillators	M-62

PHYSICAL PENDULA
My-1.	Reversible Pendulum	M-63
My-2.	Kater's Pendulum	M-63
My-3.	Oscillating Ring	M-63
My-4.	Center of Percussion and Center of Oscillation	M-63
My-5.	Center of Percussion	M-64
My-6.	Falling Chimney	M-64
My-7.	Baseball Bat	M-64
My-8.	Cork Physical Pendulum	M-64

OTHER TYPES OF OSCILLATORS
Mz-1.	Torsion Pendulum	M-65
Mz-2.	Inertia Balance	M-65
Mz-3.	Rigid and Non-Rigid Motions	M-65
Mz-4.	Oscillating Chain	M-66
Mz-5.	Oscillating Mercury Column	M-66
Mz-6.	Foucault Pendulum	M-66
Mz-7.	Model of Foucault Pendulum	M-67
Mz-8.	Dynamic Stability	M-67
Mz-9.	Upside-Down Pendulum	M-67

ELASTIC PROPERTIES OF SOLIDS
MA-1.	Crystal Model	M-67
MA-2.	Close Packed Crystals	M-68
MA-3.	Crystal Structure	M-68
MA-4.	Water Molecules and Ice Crystals	M-69
MA-5.	Faults in a Crystal	M-70
MA-6.	Bologna Bottle	M-70
MA-7.	Crushing a Salt Crystal	M-70
MA-8.	Shear of a Big Book	M-71
MA-9.	Shear of a Sponge	M-71
MA-10.	Elastic Limit	M-71

MA-11.	Poisson's Ratio	M-72
MA-12.	Modulus of Rigidity	M-72
MA-13.	Bending and Twisting	M-72

FLUIDS

GRAVITATIONAL PRESSURE
Fa-1.	Pressure Independent of Direction	F- 3
Fa-2.	Pascal Vases	F- 3
Fa-3.	Pascal Vases	F- 3
Fa-4.	Wasser Wage	F- 3

CONFINED FLUIDS
Fb-1.	Pascal Fountain	F- 4
Fb-2.	Pascal Fountain	F- 4
Fb-3.	Force and Pressure	F- 4

CHANGING PRESSURE
Fc-1.	Water Pressure	F- 4
Fc-2.	Hero's Fountain	F- 5

AIR PRESSURE
Fd-1.	Crush Can with Pressure	F- 5
Fd-2.	Magdeburg Hemispheres	F- 5
Fd-3.	Weight of a Barometer	F- 6
Fd-4.	Low Barometric Pressure	F- 6

SIPHONS
Fe-1.	Ordinary Siphon	F- 6
Fe-2.	Intermittant Siphon	F- 7
Fe-3.	Mariotte Flask and Siphon	F- 7

PRESSURE DETECTION
Ff-1.	Bourdon Gauge	F- 7
Ff-2.	Aneroid Barometer	F- 7
Ff-3.	Constant Height of a Barometer	F- 8

BUOYANCY
Fg-1.	Archimedes' Principle	F- 8
Fg-2.	Buoyancy of Hot and Cold Water	F- 8
Fg-3.	Buoyancy of Air	F- 9
Fg-4.	Loss of Weight in Water	F- 9
Fg-5.	Battleship in a Cup of Water	F- 9
Fg-6.	Cartesian Diver	F- 9
Fg-7.	Nicholson Balance	F-10

SPECIFIC GRAVITY OF FLUIDS
Fh-1.	Comparison of Fluid Densities	F-10
Fh-2.	Specific Gravity of Fluids	F-10

SURFACE TENSION
Fi-1.	Submerged Float	F-10
Fi-2.	Wet Mop	F-11
Fi-3.	Soap Bubbles	F-11
Fi-4.	Cylindrical Soap Film	F-11
Fi-5.	Mercury Amoeba	F-11
Fi-6.	Surface Reaction	F-12
Fi-7.	Force on a Film	F-12
Fi-8.	Capillary Tubes	F-12
Fi-9.	Surface Tension Hyperbola	F-12
Fi-10.	Cohesion Plates	F-13
Fi-11.	Depression and Rise in a Capillary Tube	F-13
Fi-12.	Spherical Oil Drop	F-13
Fi-13.	Ring and Thread	F-13
Fi-14.	Size of Drops	F-14
Fi-15.	Determination of Drop Size	F-14

| Fi-16. | Leaky Boats (Sieves and Razor Blades) | F-14 |
| Fi-17. | Surface Tension Boats | F-15 |

PRESSURE CHANGE WITH FLOW

Fj-1.	Bernoulli Tubes	F-15
Fj-2.	Atomizer	F-15
Fj-3.	Curved Ball Trajectory	F-15
Fj-4.	Funnel and Ball	F-16
Fj-5.	Lifting Plate	F-16
Fj-6.	Sticking Paper Flap	F-16
Fj-7.	Pressure Drop Along a Line	F-16
Fj-8.	Constriction in Pipes	F-17
Fj-9.	Floating Objects in Jet Stream	F-17
Fj-10.	Loop the Loop	F-17
Fj-11.	Pitot Tube	F-18

FLOW RATES

Fk-1.	Mariotte Flask	F-18
Fk-2.	Velocity of Efflux	F-18
Fk-3.	Turbulent Flow	F-18

CIRCULATION CONDITIONS

Fl-1.	Wind Tunnel	F-19
Fl-2.	Bottle and Candle	F-19
Fl-3.	Gravitational Pressure in Circulation	F-19
Fl-4.	Central Pressure Gradients	F-20
Fl-5.	Einstein's Birthday Present	F-20
Fl-6.	Falling Bubble	F-20
Fl-7.	Inertial Pressure Gradient	F-20

VISCOSITY

Fm-1.	Terminal Velocity	F-21
Fm-2.	Viscosity of Oil	F-21
Fm-3.	Viscosity of Gas Independent of Pressure	F-21
Fm-4.	Dependence of Viscosity on Temperature	F-22

BULK PROPERTY OF LIQUIDS

| Fn-1. | Compressibility of Water | F-22 |

DROP GROWTH

| Fo-1. | Growing a Large Drop | F-22 |

VORTEX MOTION

Fp-1.	Vortex Rings	F-23
Fp-2.	Tornado Vortex	F-23
Fp-3.	Benard Cell	F-23

HEAT

TEMPERATURE AND EXPANSION

Ha-1.	Mercury Thermometer	H- 3
Ha-2.	Gas Thermometer	H- 3
Ha-3.	Constant Volume Thermometer	H- 3
Ha-4.	Constant Volume Thermometer	H- 3
Ha-5.	Bimetal Strip	H- 3
Ha-6.	Thermostat	H- 4
Ha-7.	Ball and Ring	H- 4
Ha-8.	Expansion of a Tube	H- 4
Ha-9.	Expansion of a Fluid by Heating	H- 4
Ha-10.	Forces Caused by Change of Length	H- 5
Ha-11.	Hopping Discs	H- 5
Ha-12.	Expansion of Fluids	H- 5
Ha-13.	Water at 4°C	H- 6

HEAT CAPACITY

| Hb-1. | Calorimeter | H- 6 |

	Hb-2.	Heat Capacity	H- 6
CONVECTION			
	Hc-1.	Convection of a Gas	H- 6
	Hc-2.	Convection of Liquids	H- 7
CONDUCTION OF HEAT			
	Hd-1.	Conduction of Heat	H- 7
	Hd-2.	Conduction of Heat	H- 7
	Hd-3.	Thermal Properties of Dewars	H- 7
	Hd-4.	Insulation with Asbestos	H- 8
	Hd-5.	Poor Thermal Conductivity of Stainless Steel	H- 8
	Hd-6.	Heat Transfer	H- 8
	Hd-7.	Davy Lamp	H- 9
	Hd-8.	Expansion of Quartz	H- 9
WORK EQUIVALENT OF HEAT			
	He-1.	Work Into Heat	H- 9
	He-2.	Fire Maker	H-10
	He-3.	Mechanical Equivalent of Heat	H-10
	He-4.	Electrical Equivalent of Heat	H-10
	He-5.	Match Lighter	H-11
	He-6.	Adiabatic Heating and Cooling	H-11
	He-7.	Flow Calorimeter	H-11
RADIATION OF HEAT			
	Hf-1.	Radiation From Different Surfaces	H-12
	Hf-2.	Hole In a Black Box	H-12
	Hf-3.	Radiation From a Black Body	H-12
	Hf-4.	Radiation From a Shiny and Black Surface	H-12
	Hf-5.	Transmission of Radiant Heat	H-13
GAS LAWS			
	Hg-1.	Gas Law with Hypodermic Syringe	H-13
	Hg-2.	Model of P-V-T Surface	H-14
	Hg-3.	Clement's and Desormes' Experiment	H-14
	Hg-4.	Elastic Properties of Gases	H-14
	Hg-5.	Ruchhardt's Experiment	H-15
KINETIC THEORY			
	Hh-1.	Model for Kinetic Theory of Gases	H-16
	Hh-2.	Model of Kinetic Pressure	H-16
	Hh-3.	Brownian Motion	H-16
	Hh-4.	Two Dimensional Kinetic Motion	H-17
	Hh-5.	Mechanical Model of Kinetic Motion	H-18
	Hh-6.	Radiometer	H-18
	Hh-7.	Mean Free Path and Pressure	H-18
	Hh-8.	Viscosity Independent of Pressure	H-18
	Hh-9.	Dependence of Viscosity on Temperature	H-18
DIFFUSION AND OSMOTIC PRESSURE			
	Hi-1.	Diffusion of Hydrogen	H-19
	Hi-2.	Diffusion of CO_2	H-19
	Hi-3.	Diffusion of Gases	H-19
	Hi-4.	Diffusion of Bromine	H-19
	Hi-5.	Diffusion in Liquids	H-20
	Hi-6.	Osmotic Pressure	H-20
	Hi-7.	Preparation of Semi-Permeable Membrane	H-20
	Hi-8.	Measurement of Osmotic Pressure	H-20
VAPOR PRESSURE			
	Hj-1.	Vapor Pressure of Liquids	H-21
	Hj-2.	Addition of Partial Pressures	H-21
	Hj-3.	Boiling at Reduced Pressure	H-21
	Hj-4.	Boiling by Cooling	H-22
	Hj-5.	Geyser	H-22
	Hj-6.	Lowering of Vapor Pressure By a Dissolved Salt	H-22

Hj-7.	Drinking Bird	H-23
Hj-8.	Cryophorous	H-23
Hj-9.	Bromine Cryophorous	H-23

CHANGE OF STATE

Hk-1.	Change of Volume with Change of State	H-23
Hk-2.	Change of Volume with Change of Temperature	H-24
Hk-3.	Change of Volume with Change of State	H-24
Hk-4.	Regelation	H-24
Hk-5.	Ice Bomb	H-24
Hk-6.	Critical Point of Carbon Dioxide	H-25
Hk-7.	Rubber at Low Temperature	H-25
Hk-8.	Mercury Hammer	H-25
Hk-9.	Lead Bell	H-26
Hk-10.	Viscous Alcohol	H-26
Hk-11.	Liquid Nitrogen Cannon	H-26

DEW POINT AND CONDENSATION

Hl-1.	Wet and Dry Bulb Thermometers	H-26
Hl-2.	Sling Psychrometer	H-27
Hl-3.	Demonstration Hair Hygrometer	H-27
Hl-4.	Dew Point Measurement	H-27
Hl-5.	Dew Point	H-28
Hl-6.	Condensation Nuclei	H-28
Hl-7.	Condensation Nuclei	H-28
Hl-8.	Expansion Chamber	H-28
Hl-9.	Condensation and Coalescence	H-29
Hl-10.	Vapor Pressure of Water	H-29
Hl-11.	Ice Nuclei	H-29
Hl-12.	Wilson Cloud Chamber	H-30
Hl-13.	Diffusion Cloud Chamber	H-30

ENTROPY CHANGES

Hm-1.	Dust Explosions	H-31
Hm-2.	Order and Disorder	H-31
Hm-3.	Hilsch Tube	H-32
Hm-4.	Thermal Properties of Rubber	H-32
Hm-5.	Rubber Band Motor	H-32

HEAT ENGINES

Hn-1.	Compressed Air Engine	H-33
Hn-2.	Liquid Nitrogen Engine	H-33
Hn-3.	Steam Engine	H-34
Hn-4.	Stirling Hot Air Engine	H-34
Hn-5.	Hero's Engine	H-35

ELECTRICITY AND MAGNETISM

ELECTROSTATICS

Ea-1.	Electrostatic Charges	E- 3
Ea-2.	Electroscope	E- 3
Ea-3.	Electrostatic Voltmeter	E- 3
Ea-4.	Electrostatic Voltmeter	E- 3
Ea-5.	Electrostatic Repulsion	E- 4
Ea-6.	Repulsion and Attraction	E- 4
Ea-7.	Charges on Conductors	E- 4
Ea-8.	Electrified Strings	E- 5
Ea-9.	Piezoelectric Pistol	E- 5
Ea-10.	Shooting Down Charge	E- 6
Ea-11.	Induction Charging	E- 6
Ea-12.	Deflection of a Water Stream	E- 6
Ea-13.	Rayleigh Fountain	E- 7

Ea-14.	Kelvin Water Dropper	E- 7
Ea-15.	Charge Propelled Loop	E- 7
Ea-16.	Methods of Electrostatic Induction	E- 8
Ea-17.	Conductivity of a "Two By Four"	E- 8
Ea-18.	Surface Charge Density	E- 9
Ea-19.	Electrophorous	E- 9
Ea-20.	Shielded Electroscope	E- 9
Ea-21.	Butterfly Net Experiment	E- 9
Ea-22.	Wimshurst Machine	E-10
Ea-23.	Surface Charge Density	E-10

MOTIONS OF IONS IN A FIELD AND CORONA

Eb-1.	Electric Fields Between Electrodes	E-11
Eb-2.	Corona Discharge	E-11
Eb-3.	Electric Wind	E-11
Eb-4.	Discharge with a Flame	E-12
Eb-5.	Electrostatic Motor	E-12
Eb-6.	Cooling With Electric Wind	E-13
Eb-7.	Lightning Rod	E-13
Eb-8.	Leyden Jar	E-13
Eb-9.	Electric Chimes	E-14
Eb-10.	Electrostatic Pinwheel	E-14
Eb-11.	Electrostatic Solar System	E-14
Eb-12.	Electrostatic Precipitator	E-15
Eb-13.	Electrical Discharge from Water Drop	E-15
Eb-14.	Effect of Charge on Surface Tension	E-15
Eb-15.	Model of Millikan Oil Drop Experiment	E-16

ELECTROSTATIC GENERATORS

Ec-1.	Electrostatic Generator	E-16
Ec-2.	Lines of Force	E-17
Ec-3.	Lines of Force	E-17
Ec-4.	Pithball Plate and Flying Balls	E-17
Ec-5.	Forces Between Electrodes	E-18
Ec-6.	Electrostatic Ping-Pong	E-18
Ec-7.	Electric Field Indicator	E-18

CHARGE STORAGE

Ed-1.	Field and Voltage	E-19
Ed-2.	Dielectrics	E-19
Ed-3.	Dissectible Condenser	E-19
Ed-4.	Breath Figures	E-20
Ed-5.	Electric Field Mill	E-20
Ed-6.	Discharge of a Capacitor	E-21
Ed-7.	Charge on a Capacitor	E-21
Ed-8.	Energy Stored in a Capacitor	E-21

CHEMICAL SOURCES OF ELECTROMOTIVE FORCE

Ee-1.	Copper Flashing of Iron	E-22
Ee-2.	Dependence of EMF on Electrode Material	E-22
Ee-3.	Crowsfoot or Gravity Cell	E-22
Ee-4.	Storage Battery	E-22

CONDUCTION OF CURRENT

Ef-1.	Conductivity of Solutions	E-23
Ef-2.	Electrolysis of Water	E-23
Ef-3.	Speed of Ions	E-23
Ef-4.	Electroplating Copper	E-24
Ef-5.	Silver Coulombmeter	E-24
Ef-6.	Gas Coulombmeter	E-24

RESISTANCE AND VOLTAGE CHANGE

Eg-1.	Model of Resistance	E-25
Eg-2.	Ohm's Law	E-25
Eg-3.	Characteristic Resistances	E-25

Eg-4.	Temperature Dependence of Resistance	E-25
Eg-5.	Positive and Negative Resistance Coefficients	E-26
Eg-6.	Wheatstone Bridge	E-26
Eg-7.	Potentiometer	E-26

DISTRIBUTION OF POWER IN CIRCUITS

Eh-1.	Series and Parallel Light Bulbs	E-27
Eh-2.	Light Bulb Wheatstone Bridge	E-27
Eh-3.	Heat and Electrical Energy	E-27
Eh-4.	Transmission of Power	E-28
Eh-5.	Fuses	E-28

FORCES AND FIELDS FROM CURRENTS

Ei-1.	Force Between Parallel Wires	E-29
Ei-2.	Dancing Spiral	E-29
Ei-3.	Interacting Solenoids	E-29
Ei-4.	Force Between Radial Wires	E-30
Ei-5.	Current Balance	E-30
Ei-6.	Interaction of Flat Coils	E-31
Ei-7.	Interaction of Flat Coil and Bar Magnet	E-31
Ei-8.	Magnetic Field Around a Long Wire	E-31
Ei-9.	Magnetic Field Around a Wire	E-32
Ei-10.	Field of a Solenoid	E-32
Ei-11.	Field of a Toroid	E-32
Ei-12.	Magnetic Force on a Wire	E-32
Ei-13.	Force on a Conducting Fluid	E-33
Ei-14.	Electromagentic Pump	E-33
Ei-15.	Barlow Wheel	E-33
Ei-16.	Hall Voltage	E-34
Ei-17.	Rotating Plasma	E-34
Ei-18.	Forces on an Electron Beam	E-35
Ei-19.	DC Motor	E-35
Ei-20.	Jumping Wire	E-35

METERS AND METER USE

Ej-1.	Elements of a Galvanometer	E-36
Ej-2.	Galvanometer with Permanent Magnet	E-36
Ej-3.	Hot Wire Ammeter	E-36
Ej-4.	Iron Vane Meter	E-36
Ej-5.	Sensitivity and Resistance of Galvanometer	E-37
Ej-6.	Converting a Galvanometer to a Voltmeter	E-37
Ej-7.	Converting a Galvanometer to an Ammeter	E-37

INDUCTION

Ek-1.	Forces Due to Induced Current	E-38
Ek-2.	Currents and Forces by Induction	E-38
Ek-3.	Direction of Induced Currents	E-38
Ek-4.	Induced Currents Due to Changing Currents	E-39
Ek-5.	Time Integral of Induced Electromotive Force	E-39
Ek-6.	Earth Inductor	E-39
Ek-7.	Iron Core in Mutual Inductance	E-40

EDDY CURRENTS

El-1.	Levitation	E-40
El-2.	Damped Pendulum	E-41
El-3.	Eddy Currents in a Pendulum	E-41
El-4.	Falling Aluminum Sheet	E-41
El-5.	Frying Egg	E-42
El-6.	Money Sorter	E-42

INDUCTION COILS AND TRANSFORMERS

Em-1.	Spark Coil	E-42
Em-2.	Primary Current Change with Secondary Load	E-43
Em-3.	Jacob's Ladder	E-43
Em-4.	Large Current Transformer	E-43

Em-5.	Dissectible Transformer	E-43
Em-6.	Phony Health Belt	E-44
Em-7.	Light Under Water	E-44
Em-8.	Induction Coil	E-45
Em-9.	Shocker	E-45
Em-10.	Single Turn Transformer	E-46
Em-11.	Induced E.M.F.	E-46
Em-12.	Jumping Ring	E-46
Em-13.	Rotating Ball	E-46

AC CIRCUIT ELEMENTS

En-1.	Series L-R-C Circuit	E-47
En-2.	Phase Shift in an L-R-C Circuit	E-47
En-3.	Variable Inductance	E-47
En-4.	Capacitive Impedance	E-48
En-5.	Current in an Inductive Circuit	E-48
En-6.	R-L Time Constant	E-48
En-7.	Time Constant of an Inductive Circuit	E-49
En-8.	Time Constant of a Capacitive Circuit	E-49
En-9.	Ringing Circuit	E-50
En-10.	RC Time Constant	E-50
En-11.	Long RC Time Constant	E-50
En-12.	L-C-R Series Circuit	E-51
En-13.	Parallel Resonance	E-52

SPECIAL CIRCUIT BOARD EXPERIMENTS (P. JOHNSON)

Eo-1.	Ohm's Law	E-53
Eo-2.	Kirchoff's Voltage Law	E-53
Eo-3.	Voltage Divider	E-54
Eo-4.	Continuity of Current	E-54
Eo-5.	Equivalent Series Resistance	E-55
Eo-6.	Equivalent Parallel Resistance	E-55
Eo-7.	Superposition of Currents	E-56
Eo-8.	Wheatstone Bridge	E-57
Eo-9.	Impedance Bridge	E-57
Eo-10.	Bridge Rectifier	E-58
Eo-11.	L/R Time Constant	E-59
Eo-12.	RC Time Constant	E-59
Eo-13.	Characteristic Times in a Series L-R-C Circuit	E-60
Eo-14.	Characteristic Times in a Parallel L-R-C Circuit	E-60
Eo-15.	Parallel AC Resonance	E-61

SPECIAL ELECTRICAL DEVICES

Ep-1.	Marx Generator	E-61
Ep-2.	Tesla Coil	E-62
Ep-3.	Space Charge From High Frequency Corona	E-62
Ep-4.	High Frequency Currents	E-63
Ep-5.	Flourescent Light Bulb in Radiation Field	E-63
Ep-6.	Betatron Action	E-63
Ep-7.	Crookes Tube	E-64
Ep-8.	Bending of an Electron Beam	E-64
Ep-9.	Paddlewheel	E-64
Ep-10.	Maltese Cross	E-65
Ep-11.	e/m for Electrons	E-65
Ep-12.	Radiation From a Dipole	E-66
Ep-13.	Lecher Wires	E-66

MOTORS AND GENERATORS

Eq-1.	Sliding Rail Inductor	E-67
Eq-2.	μ Metal Shield	E-67
Eq-3.	μ Metal Shield and Insulator	E-67
Eq-4.	Motor Generator	E-68
Eq-5.	Motor Generator	E-68

Eq-6.	Series and Parallel Motors	E-69
Eq-7.	Hand Cranked Generator	E-69

PERMANENT MAGNETS

Er-1.	Interaction of Permanent Magnet and Coil	E-69
Er-2.	Interaction Between Bar Magnets	E-69
Er-3.	Period of a Bar Magnet	E-70
Er-4.	Field of a Magnet	E-70
Er-5.	Lodestone	E-70
Er-6.	Compass	E-70
Er-7.	Dip Needle	E-70
Er-8.	Magnetization in the Earth's Field	E-71
Er-9.	Permalloy Bar	E-71
Er-10.	Magnetic Suspension	E-71
Er-11.	Levitation of Magnetic Discs	E-71
Er-12.	Forming New Magnetic Poles	E-72
Er-13.	Magnetic Monopole	E-72

PROPERTIES OF MAGNETIC MATERIALS

Es-1.	Barkhausen Effect	E-72
Es-2.	Magnetic Domains	E-72
Es-3.	Paramagnetism	E-73
Es-4.	Paramagnetism	E-73
Es-5.	Magnetic Force	E-73
Es-6.	Curie Point	E-74
Es-7.	Phase Change in Iron	E-74
Es-8.	Curie Temperature	E-74
Es-9.	Magnent and Non-Magnet	E-75
Es-10	Hysteresis Loop	E-75
Es-11	Magnetic Holding with a Small Battery	E-75

THERMOELECTRIC EFFECTS

Et-1.	Thermocouple	E-76
Et-2.	Thermoelectric Cooler	E-76
Et-3.	Thermoelectric Magnet	E-76
Et-4.	3M Aztec Lamp	E-77

SOUND

WAVES

Sa-1.	Coupled Pendulums	S- 3
Sa-2.	Projection Coupled Pendula	S- 3
Sa-3.	Wave Pulse on a Rope	S- 3
Sa-4.	Water Wave Model of Phase Velocity	S- 3
Sa-5.	Standing Pulse	S- 4
Sa-6.	Traveling Waves	S- 4
Sa-7.	Wave Reflection at a Discontinuity	S- 5
Sa-8.	Traveling and Standing Waves	S- 5
Sa-9.	Standing Waves	S- 5
Sa-10.	Melde's Experiment	S- 6
Sa-11.	Speed of Wave Greater Than Speed of Particles	S- 6
Sa-12.	Wave Pulses in a Slinky Spring	S- 6
Sa-13.	Waves on an Air Track	S- 7
Sa-14.	Slinky Spring	S- 7
Sa-15.	Crova's Disc	S- 7
Sa-16.	Flaming Tube	S- 8
Sa-17.	Kundt's Tube	S- 8
Sa-18.	Noisey Kundt's Tube with Hot Wire	S- 8

STANDING WAVES IN PLATES

Sb-1.	Chladni Plates	S- 9
Sb-2.	Two Dimensional Birthday Cake	S- 9

	Sb-3.	Forced Nodes and Loops in a Vibrating Plate	S- 9
SOUND SOURCES			
	Sc-1.	Siren Disc	S-10
	Sc-2.	Musical Saw	S-10
	Sc-3.	Quadropole Nature of a Tuning Fork	S-10
	Sc-4.	Intensity of Sound	S-10
RESONANCE			
	Sd-1.	Resonance Pendula	S-11
	Sd-2.	Frequency Meter	S-11
	Sd-3.	Tuned Resonance Box	S-11
RESONANCE IN PIPES			
	Se-1.	Resonance Tube	S-12
	Se-2.	Tuned Bottles	S-12
	Se-3.	Helmholtz Resonators	S-12
	Se-4.	Musical Bottles	S-13
	Se-5.	Hoot Tube	S-13
	Se-6.	Freq Tube	S-13
	Se-7.	Freq Tube Dash Pot	S-13
	Se-8.	Musical Goblets	S-13
	Se-9.	Organ Pipe	S-14
	Se-10.	Variable Pitch Whistle	S-14
	Se-11.	"C" Bazooka	S-14
VIBRATING BARS			
	Sf-1.	Tuning Forks with Resonators	S-14
	Sf-2.	Vowel Tuning Forks	S-14
	Sf-3.	Transmission of Sound Through Wood	S-15
	Sf-4.	Ultasonic Waves	S-15
	Sf-5.	Glockenspiel	S-15
	Sf-6.	Musical Sticks	S-15
INTERFERNECE OF SOUND WAVES			
	Sg-1.	Galton Whistle	S-16
	Sg-2.	Directional Transmission of Short Wavelength Sound	S-16
	Sg-3.	Diffraction of Sound	S-16
	Sg-4.	Interference of Sound	S-17
SOUND WAVES			
	Sh-1.	Wavelength of Sound in Air	S-17
	Sh-2.	No Sound Through Vacuum	S-17
	Sh-3.	Range of Hearing	S-18
	Sh-4.	Low Frequency Tuning Fork	S-18
DOPPLER SHIFT AND BEATS			
	Si-1.	Doppler Shift	S-18
	Si-2.	Doppler Shift with Reed	S-18
	Si-3.	Doppler Shift from Turntable	S-19
	Si-4.	Beat Bars	S-19
	Si-5.	Beat Whistles	S-20
	Si-6.	Beats with a Light Beam	S-20
	Si-7.	Churchbell Guitar	S-20
VIBRATING STRINGS			
	Sj-1.	Sonometer	S-21
	Sj-2.	Mode of String Oscillation	S-21
	Sj-3.	Harmonics of a String	S-22
	Sj-4.	Harmonious Notes	S-22
	Sj-5.	Chords	S-23
	Sj-6.	One String Violin	S-23
MUSICAL SYNTHESIS			
	Sk-1.	Musical Scales	S-24
	Sk-2.	Circular Glockenspiel	S-25
	Sk-3.	Electronic Synthesizer	S-25

HEARING AND SOUND WAVES
    Sl-1.   Binaural Hearing   S-26
    Sl-2.   Phase and Group Velocity   S-26
    Sl-3.   Interference of Sound Waves   S-26
WATER WAVE MODELS
    Sm-1.   Ripple Tank   S-27
    Sm-2.   Double Source   S-27
    Sm-3.   Plane Waves   S-27
    Sm-4.   Single Slit   S-27
    Sm-5.   Double Slit   S-28
    Sm-6.   Action of a Lens   S-28
LISSAJOUS FIGURES
    Sn-1.   Lissajous Figures in Sand   S-28
    Sn-2.   Sand Track Lissajous Figures   S-29
    Sn-3.   Lissajous Figures on an Oscilloscope   S-29
    Sn-4.   Lissajous Coordinate System   S-30
TIME MEASUREMENT
    So-1.   Metronome   S-30

OPTICS

STRAIGHT LINE PROPAGATION OF LIGHT
    Oa-1.   Straight Line Propagation of Light   O- 3
    Oa-2.   Pinhole Projection   O- 3
    Oa-3.   Pinhole Camera   O- 3
    Oa-4.   Velocity of Light   O- 4
PLANE MIRRORS AND REFLECTION
    Ob-1.   Reflection From Smooth and Rough Surfaces   O- 5
    Ob-2.   Position of Image   O- 5
    Ob-3.   Height of Mirror for Full View   O- 5
    Ob-4.   Mirrors at an Angle   O- 6
    Ob-5.   Parallel Mirrors   O- 6
    Ob-6.   Straight Back Reflector   O- 6
    Ob-7.   Inverted Image   O- 6
    Ob-8.   Optical Disc   O- 7
    Ob-9.   Perversion   O- 7
    Ob-10.   Elliptical Tank   O- 7
    Ob-11.   Blackboard Optics-Plane Mirror   O- 7
REFLECTION FROM CURVED SURFACES
    Oc-1.   Blackboard Optics-Concave Mirror   O- 8
    Oc-2.   Blackboard Optics-Convex Mirror   O- 8
    Oc-3.   Optical Disc-Curved Mirror   O- 8
    Oc-4.   Image with a Concave Mirror   O- 8
    Oc-5.   Amusement Park Mirrors   O- 9
    Oc-6.   Red Ball in Mirror   O- 9
    Oc-7.   Find the Object   O- 9
    Oc-8.   No Image with a Convex Mirror   O-10
    Oc-9.   Lighting a Cigarette   O-10
    Oc-10.   Image of a Flower in a Vase   O-10
    Oc-11.   Cold Candle   O-10
REFRACTION AT A PLANE SURFACE
    Od-1.   Refraction at the Surface of Water   O-11
    Od-2.   Blackboard Optics-Refraction   O-11
    Od-3.   Law of Refraction   O-11
    Od-4.   Seeing a Coin   O-12
    Od-5.   Broken Stick   O-12
    Od-6.   Apparent Depth   O-12
    Od-7.   Index of Refraction by Apparent Depth   O-12

CRITICAL ANGLE
 Oe-1. Critical Angle   O-13
 Oe-2. Light Below Surface   O-13
 Oe-3. Black Ball Turns Silver   O-13
 Oe-4. Mercury in a Test Tube   O-13
 Oe-5. Total Reflection from Water Surface O-13
 Oe-6. Light Scattering from Ice   O-14
 Oe-7. Light Pipe   O-14
LIGHT THROUGH PRISMS
 Of-1. Minimum Deviation of a Prism O-14
 Of-2. Inversion of Image   O-15
 Of-3. Double Reflection at the Critical Angle O-15
 Of-4. Double Reflection in Two Dimensions O-15
LENSES
 Og-1. Optical Disc-Refreaction at Curved Surfaces O-16
 Og-2. Water Lens   O-16
 Og-3. Diverging Beam   O-16
 Og-4. Optical Disc-Circular Glass Plate O-16
 Og-5. Thin Convex Lens   O-17
 Og-6. Thin Concave Lens   O-17
 Og-7. Blackboard Optics-Thin Lenses O-17
 Og-8. Model of the Eye   O-18
 Og-9. Light Rays Through Lenses   O-18
 Og-10. Optical Disc-Lenses   O-19
 Og-11. Watch Glass Lens   O-19
 Og-12. Focal Length of a Lens   O-20
 Og-13. Changing Beam Size Without Inversion O-20
USING LENSES
 Oh-1. Aberration   O-21
 Oh-2. Improving an Image with a Stop O-21
 Oh-3. Depth of Focus   O-22
 Oh-4. Use of Cross Hairs and Superposition of Images O-22
INTENSITY OF LIGHT
 Oi-1. Inverse Square Law   O-23
 Oi-2. Rumford Photometer   O-23
 Oi-3. Grease Spot Photometer   O-23
 Oi-4. Paraffin Block Photometer   O-24
 Oi-5. Radiation Laws   O-24
 Oi-6. Surface Brightness   O-25
 Oi-7. Surface Brightness of a Reflecting Surface O-25
 Oi-8. Surface Brightness of a Lens   O-25
 Oi-9. Integration of Light Pulses by the Eye O-25
 Oi-10. Jarring the Eyeball   O-26
 Oi-11. Eye Most Sensitive to Green Light O-26
 Oi-12. Retinal Fatigue   O-26
SPECTRUM AND COLOR
 Oj-1. Purity of the Spectrum   O-27
 Oj-2. Synthesis of Colors   O-27
 Oj-3. Color Box   O-27
 Oj-4. Recombining the Spectrum   O-27
 Oj-5. Dispersion of Liquids   O-28
 Oj-6. Dispersion in Different Media   O-28
 Oj-7. Deviation with No Dispersion   O-28
 Oj-8. Dispersion with No Deviation   O-29
 Oj-9. Chromatic Aberration in a Lens O-29
 Oj-10. Rainbow   O-29
ULTRAVIOLET LIGHT
 Ok-1. Ultraviolet Light   O-30
 Ok-2. Black Light   O-30

Ok-3.	Photoelectric Effect	O-30
Ok-4.	Photoelectric Effect Produced with Ultraviolet Light	O-30

ELECTROMAGNETIC WAVE PROPERTIES OF LIGHT

Ol-1.	Wave Nature of Electromagnetic Radiation	O-31
Ol-2.	Single Slit Diffraction-Radar	O-31
Ol-3.	Single Slit Diffraction of Light	O-31
Ol-4.	Radar Interference Using Two Slits	O-32
Ol-5.	Light Interfenence Using Two Slits	O-32
Ol-6.	Single Slit Diffraction Pattern	O-32
Ol-7.	Adjustable Slit	O-33
Ol-8.	Photodiode Receiver Array	O-33
Ol-9.	Interference Pattern of Two Slits	O-33
Ol-10.	Number of Slits	O-34
Ol-11.	Fresnel Biprism	O-34
Ol-12.	Billet Half Lens	O-34
Ol-13.	Two Dimensional Grating	O-34
Ol-14.	Model of Crystal Lattice	O-35
Ol-15.	Interference in Thin Sheets	O-35
Ol-16.	Soap Film Interference	O-36
Ol-17.	Newton's Rings	O-36
Ol-18.	Air Wedge	O-36
Ol-19.	Michelson Interferometer	O-37
Ol-20.	Michelson Interferometer with Radar	O-38
Ol-21.	Diffraction	O-38
Ol-22.	Fresnel Zones	O-39
Ol-23.	Zone Plate Lens	O-39

POLARIZATION

Om-1.	Polarization of Electromagnetic Waves	O-40
Om-2.	Polarization of Light by Reflection	O-40
Om-3.	Crystal Models	O-40
Om-4.	Optic Axis and Index Ellipsoids	O-41
Om-5.	Ordinary and Extraordinary Ray	O-41
Om-6.	Polarization of Ordinary and Extraordinary Rays	O-41
Om-7.	Nicol Prism	O-42
Om-8.	Nicol Prisms as Polarizer and Analyzer	O-42
Om-9.	Polaroids as Polarizer and Analyzer	O-42
Om-10.	Half-Wave Plate	O-43
Om-11.	Quarter Wave Plate	O-43
Om-12.	Crystal Structure in Ice	O-44
Om-13.	Crystal Growth in a Film	O-44
Om-14.	Changing Colored Designs with Polarized Light	O-45
Om-15.	Polarization witha Slide Projector	O-45
Om-16.	Polarization by Karo Syrup	O-46
Om-17.	Black Glass Polarizer-Analyzer	O-46
Om-18.	Polarization by a Cone	O-46
Om-19.	Circularly Polarized Radiation	O-47

LIGHT SCATTERING

On-1.	Light Scattering	O-47
On-2.	Polarization of Scattered Light	O-47

ABSORBTION AND EMISSION OF LIGHT

Oo-1.	Resonance Radiation	O-48
Oo-2.	Mercury Vapor Shadow	O-48
Oo-3.	Dark Line Spectra	O-48
Oo-4.	Absorbtion Lines of Sodium	O-49

BEAM SCATTERING

Op-1.	Schieren Image	O-49

MODERN PHYSICS

NUCLEAR REACTIONS
    MPa-1.   Mousetrap Chain Reaction   MP-3
    MPa-2.   Geiger Counter   MP-3
INTERACTION OF LIGHT WITH MATTER
    MPb-1.   Photoelectric Effect   MP-4
RADIATION IN MAGNETIC FIELDS
    MPc-1.   Zeeman Splitting   MP-5

Note to Users

As stated in the preface, this
handbook is meant to describe and
illustrate some of the experiments
which can be used to demonstrate
physical phenomena. No actual
numerical values are given. This
handbook has been designed with
large margins so that each user of
it can record data relevant to his
particular experimental arrangement of the demonstrations he
chooses to show.

MECHANICS

Ma-1. LENGTH

Copies of the standard meter and standard yard can be placed on the lecture table for examination by the students.

Ma-2. MASS

Sets of calibrated weights in metric and English units may be placed on the lecture table. By using brass weights one can also show the relative size of the pound and the kilogram. In order to establish the concept of magnitudes in the metric system one may weigh a few coins.

Ma-3. TIME

The students can listen to the time signals from W W V. The frequency signals may be displayed on a oscilloscope.

A motor driven model of the sun, moon, earth system may be shown. The difference between sidereal and solar days can easily be demonstrated. The orbits are all circular so the concept of a mean solar day can only be discussed.

Mb-1. REACTION TIME

(A)

(A). A Large stop clock reading to 1/100sec is used for most time measurements. In order to measure reaction time and its effect on measurements one can hide the sweep hand behind a disc of cardboard with one quadrant cut out. Students are asked to find how close to the emerging point they can stop the sweep hand.

(B)

(B). A second measure of reaction time can be made with a falling meter stick. One observer may place his opened fingers at some known mark along the stick. A second person then drops the stick at an arbitrary time. The distance fallen can be converted to a reaction time. A variation of this is to use a dollar bill folded lengthwise. It is a safe bet that one cannot catch the bill if it starts initially between the fingers of the catcher.

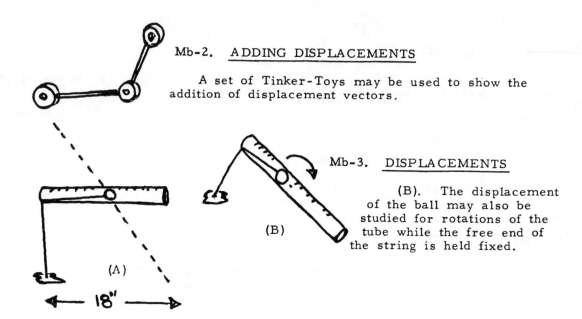

Mb-2. ADDING DISPLACEMENTS

A set of Tinker-Toys may be used to show the addition of displacement vectors.

Mb-3. DISPLACEMENTS

(B). The displacement of the ball may also be studied for rotations of the tube while the free end of the string is held fixed.

(B)

(A)

← 18" →

(A). A glass tube containg a ball and string is laid flat on the lecture table. With one end of the string held to the lecture table the glass tube is raised horizontally. The simultaneous upward and lateral displacement with the resultant diagonal displacement is quite apparent.

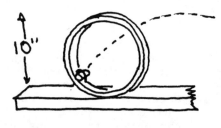

10"

Mb-4. CYCLOIDAL MOTION

A 10 inch diameter hoop has a piece of chalk fastened to the circumference. The hoop is then rolled along the chalk tray of the classroom blackboard to show the cycloidal motion. This demonstration helps the students visualize more easily that the velocity is zero at the cusps.

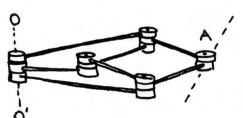

O

A

O'

Mb-5. INVERSOR

Rotational motion about the axis OO' makes "A" have rectilinear motion.

Mb-6. ROTATION AND RELATIVE TRANSLATION

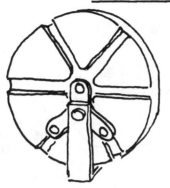

The small three pronged
spider could be freely rotated
because its pegs slide back
and forth in the grooves of
the six slotted wheel.

Mb-7. DIFFERENTIAL MOTION

String is wrapped onto two different
sized pullies. The pullies are joined
on a common axis. The strings unwind
from the two pullies at different rates
so that the frame for the pullies is
raised or lowered by pulling on the
strings. The device is usually made
in the form of a toy climbing monkey
or toy pirate.

Mb-8. ROTATION AND TRANSLATION

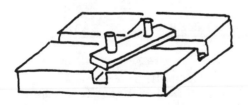

The small block with
pins running in crossed
slots in the base can
rotate.

Mb-9. DISTANCE AND TIME INTERVALS

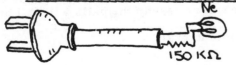

A neon bulb is placed
in series with a 150KΩ
resistor at the end of a
lamp cord. When the cord
is swung around ones head in
a circular path, a dot to dot trajectory is observed.

Mb-10. AVERAGE AND INSTANTANEOUS VELOCITY

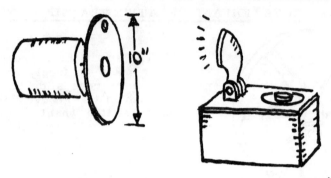

A 1725 R.P.M. motor carries a fluorescent marker on a connected disc. The system is viewed with a stroboscope running at various multiples of the frequency. Displacements, $\overrightarrow{\Delta S}$, can be measured on the disc and corresponding times, Δt , are read from the stroboscope. Instantaneous velocity as a limiting process may be studied.

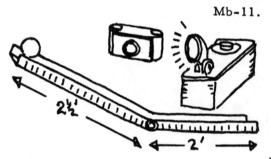

Mb-11. UNIFORM AND ACCELERATED MOTION

An inclined track is joined to a horizontal track by a phosphor bronze strip so that any angle of tilt may be formed. A ball then rolls down the track while illuminated with a stroboscope. Accelerated and uniform motion may be compared. A time exposure with a Polaroid camera and transparent film may be made and projected for the entire class to see. A scale is placed on the track to measure distances. The stroboscope may be run at different speeds to show the limiting process of obtaining instantaneous velocities.

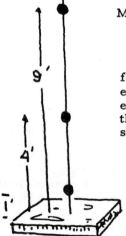

Mb-12. TIME INTERVALS OF FALL

A long string of balls is constructed as follows. The first ball is 1 foot from the bottom end, the second ball is 4 feet from the bottom end, the third is 9 feet from the bottom, and the fourth ball is 16 feet from the end. The string of balls is suspended from the ceiling directly above a resonant board. When the string is released, the balls will fall onto the resonant board and sound out at regular time intervals.

Mb-13. UNIFORM ACCELERATION

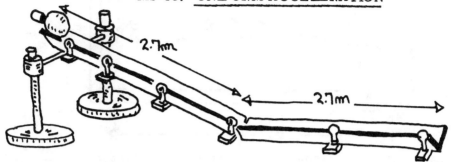

A hinged "V" track with two 2.7 meter sections is constructed
of stock aluminum. Small lights are mounted along the track
which flash at regular time intervals. A two inch steel ball is
held at the top end of the track by an electromagnet. The
magnent release is synchronized with the flashing lights. The
slope of the track is adjusted so that the ball is at the position
of successive lights at the time of each flash. For circuitry see
N. J. Petit and P. A. Johnson,
Am. J. Phys. 47, 287 (1979).

Mb-14.   SIMULTANEOUS FALL

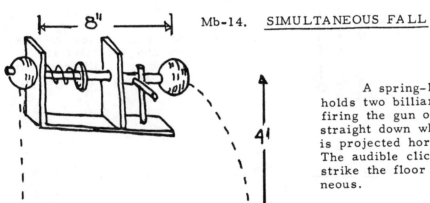

A spring-loaded gun
holds two billiard balls. On
firing the gun one ball falls
straight down while the other
is projected horizontally.
The audible clicks when they
strike the floor are simultaneous.

Mb-15.   TIME OF FLIGHT

If one juggles, the rate of motion of
one's hands is inversely proportional to the
time of flight. Low trajectories require fast
juggling while high trajectories allow one to
juggle slowly.

Mb-16. MONKEY AND CANNON

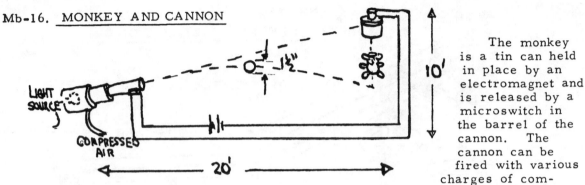

The monkey is a tin can held in place by an electromagnet and is released by a microswitch in the barrel of the cannon. The cannon can be fired with various charges of compressed air. Before placing the projectile in the cannon, the aiming is done with an optical system built into the cannon. The cannon is then loaded and fired. The professor should learn carefully the switching arrangements so he does not drop the monkey while loading the cannon.

Mb-17. TRAJECTORY MODEL

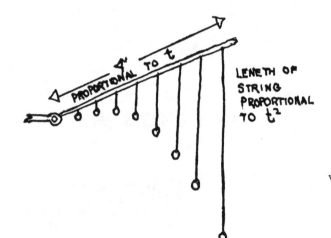

A pivoted bar has pendulums attached at equal intervals. The length of each pendulum is proportional to the square of its distance from the pivot point. The bar may then be raised and lowered to show various parabolic trajectories corresponding to different initial velocities.

Mb-18. MEASUREMENT OF "g"

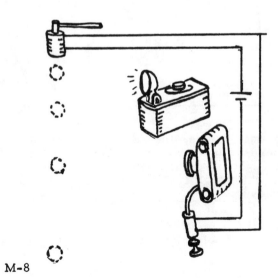

A ball is held with an electromagnet and can be released by a microswitch in the camera shutter release. A time exposure is made with the light produced by a stroboscope. If one uses a Polaroid camera with transparent film, the picture may be developed and projected for presentation of the data to the class. A meter stick should be in the picture to establish the correct scale.

Mb-19. WATER TRAJECTORY

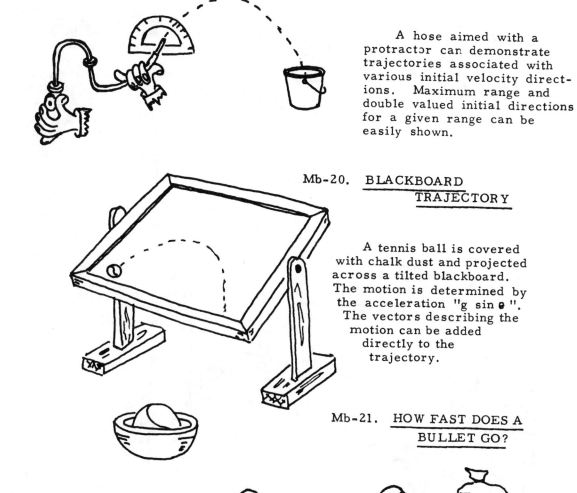

A hose aimed with a protractor can demonstrate trajectories associated with various initial velocity directions. Maximum range and double valued initial directions for a given range can be easily shown.

Mb-20. BLACKBOARD TRAJECTORY

A tennis ball is covered with chalk dust and projected across a tilted blackboard. The motion is determined by the acceleration "g sin θ". The vectors describing the motion can be added directly to the trajectory.

Mb-21. HOW FAST DOES A BULLET GO?

A timer or oscilloscope is used to measure the time duration a Wheatstone bridge is unbalanced by a bullet aimed to break two metal foils in succession.

Mb-22. <u>VELOCITY OF A BULLET</u>

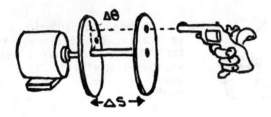

The velocity of an air gun pellet may be determined by firing a shot through parallel rotating cardboard discs. The distance ΔS is measured directly and the time is determined from the angular displacement of the holes and the angular velocity of the motor.

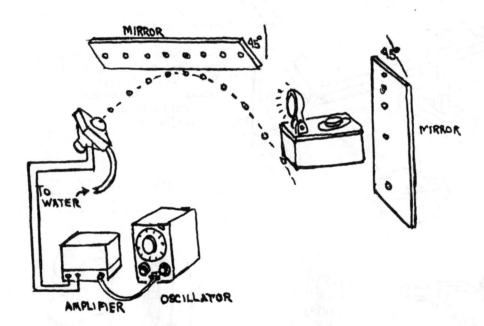

Mb-23. OBTAINING "g" FROM A TRAJECTORY

A stream of regularly spaced water droplets is obtained from a loudspeaker driven nozzle. The spacing of the droplets is adjusted with an oscillator and audio amplifier which drives the speaker. The water supply should come from a constant level reservoir. Mirrors are placed horizontally and vertically at 45°. The horizontal mirror shows the equal spacing of the drops due to their uniform motion while the vertical mirror shows the drop spacing due to accelerated motion. The stroboscope is first synchronized with the oscillator so that all drops appear to be stationary at a frequency f_1. The stroboscope frequency is then shifted by Δf so that all the drops move slowly. The apparent time of fall through a certain distance is measured with a stopwatch from which one can calculate an apparent value of g'. The value of g is then found by the equation $g = g' \left(\frac{\Delta f}{f_1} \right)^{-2}$. (See <u>Am. J. Phys.</u>, <u>37</u>, 929, (1969).)

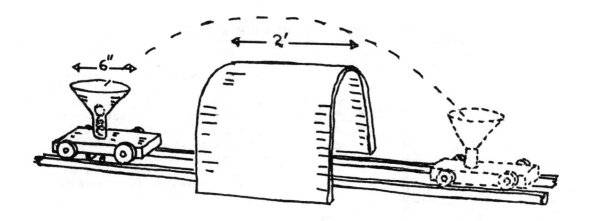

Mb-24. HOWITZER AND TUNNEL

A cart is mounted on horizontal rails so that it can maintain a uniform
velocity after an initial shove. It carries a cannon which fires a projectile
vertically and catches it again in a flared end on the barrel. A triggering
switch on the rails can fire the cannon while the cart is in motion. Now if
the cart is given a horizontal velocity the projectile can go over the tunnel
while the cart goes through it and then catches the projectile on the far side.

Mb-25. CORIOLIS ACCELERATION

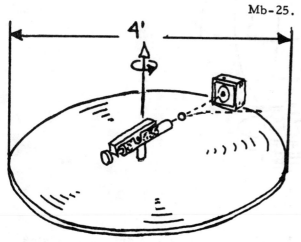

A spring-loaded gun which fires
a 3/8" ball bearing is mounted at
the center of a turntable which
rotates freely when given a spin.
The pellet is first fired when the
system is at rest and a mark is
obtained on the target. The gun
is then fired when the system is
rotating by hitting the catch on
the gun from above with a hammer.
The mark of the pellet now falls
to the trailing edge of the moving
target.

Mb-26.   CORIOLIS ACCELERATION WITH WATER

A can of water is mounted off the axis of a large turntable. There is a small hole in the side of the can. The stream of water falls in a parabolic trajectory when the turntable is at rest. If the turntable is rotating, the water stream is deflected out of a vertical plane by the Coriolis force.

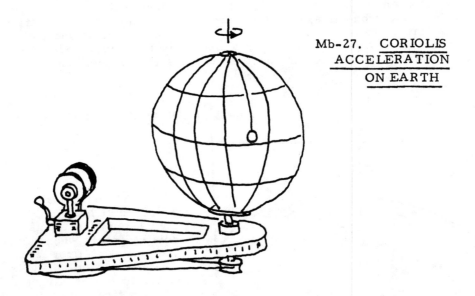

Mb-27.   CORIOLIS ACCELERATION ON EARTH

A large globe with a hollow shaft for an axis is driven at a slow rotation rate by an electric motor in the direction that the Earth rotates. A string is threaded through the axis and fastened to a lead ball which can then be moved across lines of latitude by pulling the string. As the ball moves on the rotating globe it will always cross meridian lines as if it is deflected to its right. This is true for motion either toward the equator or toward the poles.

Mb-28. ACCELERATED COORDINATE SYSTEM

A piece of white cardboard is attached to the surface of a motor driven turntable. A guide bar is mounted over the top along a diameter. When the table is in motion a felt pen is moved uniformly along the guide bar. Many interesting curved patterns are traced on the paper depending on the magnitude of the uniform motion along the guide bar. The fact that the traces are curved is sufficient to prove there is acceleration in the rotating coordinate system.

Mb-29. CENTRAL ACCELERATION

A pail containing water is whirled in a vertical circle without spilling the water when the central acceleration is equal to or greater than the acceleration due to gravity.

Mb-30. RELATIVE VELOCITY

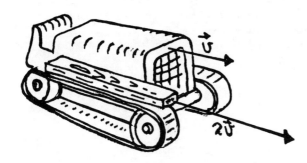

A small board is placed on the top tread of a toy Caterpillar tractor. The board moves with velocity 2υ while the tractor moves with velocity υ. This demonstrates that the top of a rolling wheel is traveling with twice the velocity of the axle.

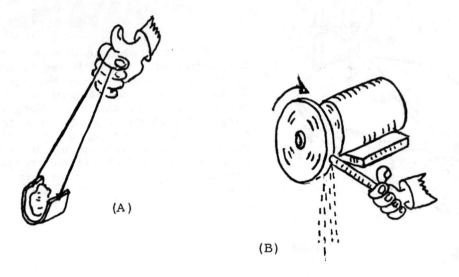

(A)

(B)

(A). A David and
Goliath type slingshot is
used to show that the velocity
continues unaltered in direction
when the central acceleration
is removed.

(B). The velocity of hot
Carborundum particles from a
grinding wheel is tangent to the
path of circular motion of the
particles when they are freed
from the wheel.

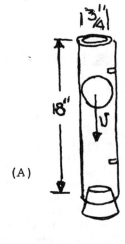

(A)

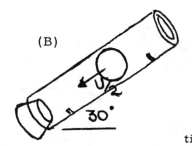

(B)

(C)

WATER

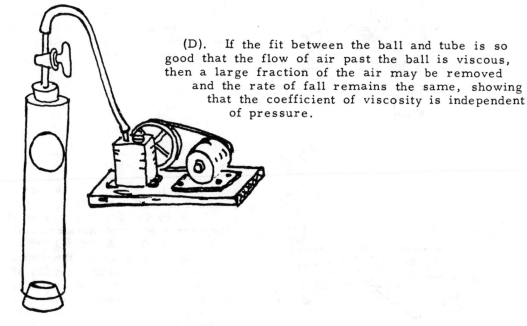

(D)

(A). A piece of precision bore glass tubing 3/4" in diameter is corked at one end. A 3/4" ball bearing will fall with a slow uniform velocity through the tube. To obtain an optimum fit, the ball bearing should be etched in a dilute solution of HCl until it slides through the tube at the desired speed. Several tape marks may be placed on the tube and the velocity of fall of the ball bearing determined from their separation and the time the ball bearing requires to move between marks. It is instructive to have the tape marks at unequal distances and then measure the unequal times to show that the ratio of distance to time remains constant.

(B). The tube and ball may be propped at 30° to the horizontal to show that the velocity becomes half as great.

(C). If the tube is filled with water, the uniform motion is very slow, i.e. hardly visible unless one watches it for a long time. Measurements show the motion to be uniform.

(D). If the fit between the ball and tube is so good that the flow of air past the ball is viscous, then a large fraction of the air may be removed and the rate of fall remains the same, showing that the coefficient of viscosity is independent of pressure.

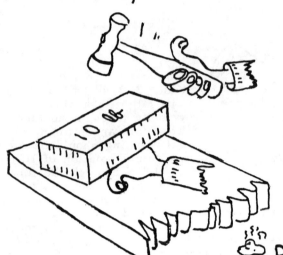

Mc-1. INERTIA OF REST

A 10 lb. steel brick is placed on one hand laying on the lecture table. A vigorous blow is given to the brick with a hammer. No apparent damage is done to the hand under the brick.

For interest one can palm a piece of dry ice and place the struck hand into a beaker of water. Tell the students that the energy loss will be discussed later. A variation of this is to place a 50 lb. lead brick on one's stomach while reclining on the lecture table. One of the lecture assistants then strikes the brick with a heavy blow of a sledge hammer. This can be done at the beginning of the lecture hour.

DRY ICE

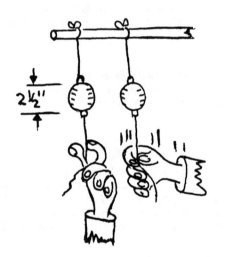

Mc-2. INERTIA BALLS

Two identical steel balls are suspended by identical threads tied to their bottoms. The first one is given a uniform downward pull of the bottom thread and the top thread always breaks. The second is given a quick jerk on the bottom thread which in turn always breaks.

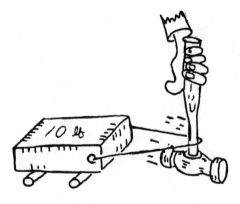

Mc-3. INERTIA BLOCK

A length of window sash cord or clothesline rope is tied in a loop through an eye in a 10 lb. block which is free to slide along the table. A uniform pull will easily drag the block. A violent jerk with a hammer will always break the rope. If one wishes, the breaking strength of the rope may be measured. The experiment may be repeated with a very fine thread to show that the block can be moved with small forces and small accelerations.

Mc-4.   INERTIA OF REST

(A). A slender steel cylinder
is placed on end onto a sheet of
paper. The paper is jerked out
without upsetting the cylinder.

(A)

(B)

(B). Instead of the cylinder
one may use a dinner setting on
a tablecloth. The tablecloth must
have no seam on the back end
which slides under the dishes.

Mc-5.   TIGHTENING A HAMMER HANDLE

A hammer handle or
axe handle may be tightened
by pounding on the far end
of the loose handle.

Md-1.   REACTION CARTS

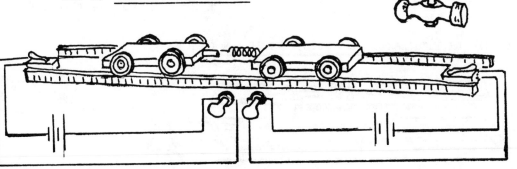

Two identical carts are placed on horizontal rails and have a spring loading
so that they can be triggered and recoil against each other. At the end of the
tracks the carts bounce from microswitches which are in series with the lights.
If the carts are triggered at the center of the board, then both lights flashing
simultaneously indicate that accelerations, velocities, and times for the two
carts were identical. A third identical cart can be placed as a rider on one
of the original two. A second switch at half the distance then shows the above
result with the heavy cart receiving one half the acceleration. Objects of
varying masses may be qualitatively tried. A teaching trick is to place one of
the carts on "Paris" as a standard and in principal all other masses could be
determined with this apparatus and this standard mass.

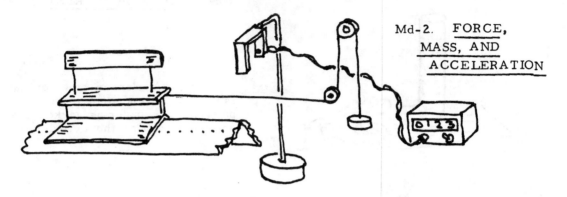

Md-2. FORCE,
MASS, AND
ACCELERATION

An air cart carries an opaque flag 10 cm long which can
pass between a photo diode and a photo receiver to interrupt
the beam of light. The time the light is off is measured on a
fast counter. The falling weight attached to the cart is always
made to fall one meter. The velocity measurement is made
after the 1 meter of fall. The velocity acquired by the weight
(and cart) for a combination of masses may be quickly
determined.

Md-3. MAGNET REACTION CARTS

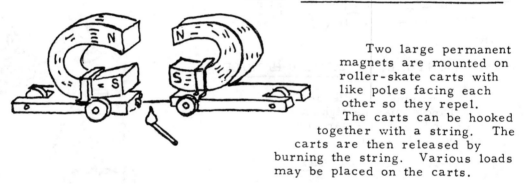

Two large permanent
magnets are mounted on
roller-skate carts with
like poles facing each
other so they repel.
The carts can be hooked
together with a string. The
carts are then released by
burning the string. Various loads
may be placed on the carts.

Md-4. ACTION AND REACTION WITH AIR CARTS

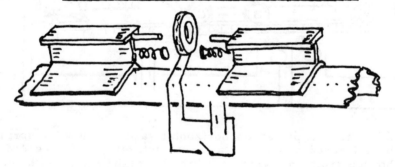

Two identical air carts are made with compressible springs
and soft iron slugs on facing ends. The springs are compressed
when the carts are forced together. The carts are held together
by energizing a coil around the iron slugs. When the switch to
coil is opened, the carts spring apart. The carts may be loaded
in various ways to show mass effects.

Me-1. PERSISTANCE OF MOTION

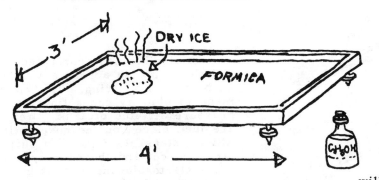

A very flat formica plane with leveling screws is placed on the lecture table. The plane is then wetted with alcohol. A piece of dry ice which has been flattened on one side will now ride over the surface with a gas lubricant having negligible friction. A very small initial push will result in motion of the dry ice that persists several times across the board.

Me-2. AIR TABLE AND PUCKS

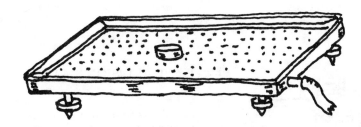

The air table has many holes so that pucks can ride on films of air. The edges of the table are made of stretched wire so the puck will make elastic collisions with the walls. All types of two dimensional collisions may be demonstrated.

Mf-1. WEIGHT OF A MASS

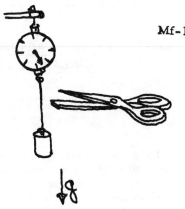

To show that the weight of an object is $m\vec{g}$, hold the weight in equilibrium with a spring balance. Cut the supporting string to remove the equilibrium force and the mass has the acceleration $\vec{g}$

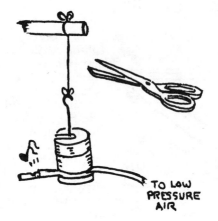

Mf-2. VANISHING WEIGHT

A flexible hose connected to a whistle is placed across a weight pan supported by a string. The whistle is made to blow by connecting it to a low pressure air line or tank. Weights are then placed on the hose until the whistle stops blowing. The supporting string is cut and the whistle immediately starts blowing. What happened to the "weight"?

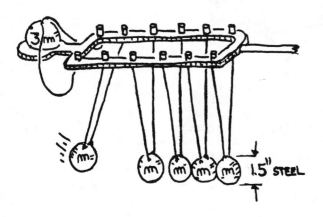

Mg-1. COLLISION BALLS

A set of identical steel balls is suspended bifilarly in a straight row. Many combinations of balls may be used to produce elastic collisions. Inelastic collisions can be realized by inserting a piece of tacky wax at the impact points. One ball of three times the mass of the others may be inserted to demonstrate a rather peculiar behavior. Students should be encouraged to try these experiments with coins on a smooth table top.

Mg-2. CONSERVATION OF LINEAR MOMENTUM

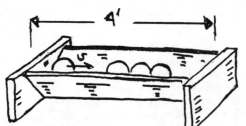

This demonstration is very much like the one above except that results aren't quite so good due to loss of rotational energy. It suggests to the student the possibility of doing this experiment in a bowling alley.

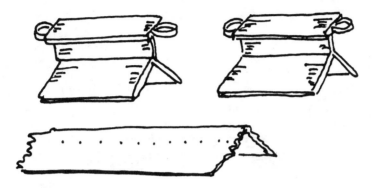

Mg-3. ELASTIC COLLISIONS WITH AIR CARTS

Air track carts are fitted with loops made of clock spring steel so that they can make elastic collisions. Carts can be weighted or made of different sizes. Various initial and final velocity conditions may be studied.

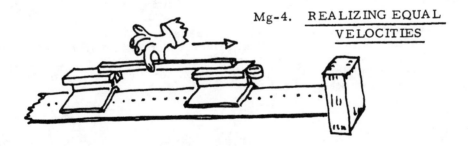

Mg-4. REALIZING EQUAL
VELOCITIES

Two air track carts have their facing collision regions covered with Velcro so that they can make an inelastic collision. The carts are initially spearated and set into motion with a meter stick laid across the tops. After some motion is given to the two carts, the meter stick is withdrawn. The first cart makes an elastic collision with the end of the air track and bounces back with reversed motion. The two carts then collide and stop in an inelastic collision.

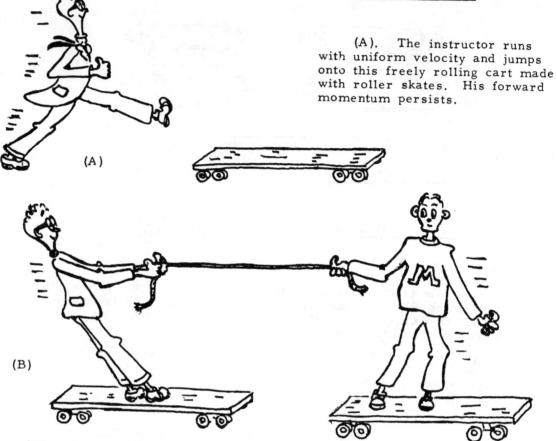

(A). The instructor runs with uniform velocity and jumps onto this freely rolling cart made with roller skates. His forward momentum persists.

(A)

(B)

(B). Two identical roller skate carts are used. A student on one cart and the instructor on the other can draw themselves together by means of a rope or push each other apart with a bamboo pole. The motion is identical for either during the pushing or pulling. Changes of motion for two, three, or four students may be demonstrated.

(C). The instructor tosses a heavy medicine ball while standing on the roller skate cart. The ball is sufficiently heavy to produce considerable recoil. Catching of the ball may also be tried.

(C)

Mh-1. ROCKET CAR

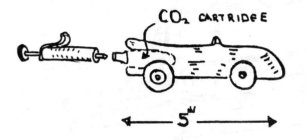

A small wooden car contains a cavity which holds a CO_2 cartridge. The cartridge is punctured with a needle-like plunger and the escaping CO_2 accelerates the car.

Mh-2. ROCKET TO THE MOON

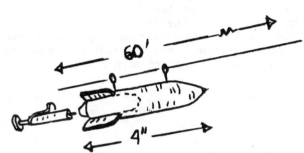

A small rocket is attached to an inclined wire strung across the lecture room. A punctured CO_2 cartridge then accelerates this across the room with a high velocity.

Mh-3. WATER ROCKET

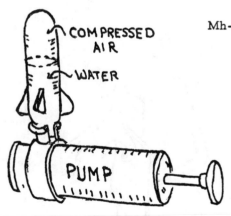

This is a commercial toy. The rocket is filled one third full of water and the remaining volume with compressed air obtained by 10 or 20 strokes of the special pump. Outside this rocket will rise to a height of 150 feet. One can compare the water discharge with the air discharge to eliminate foolish thoughts about pressure alone being responsible for this phenomenon.

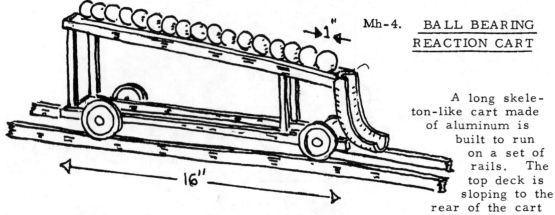

Mh-4. BALL BEARING
REACTION CART

A long skele-
ton-like cart made
of aluminum is
built to run
on a set of
rails. The
top deck is
sloping to the
rear of the cart
and is terminated by a chute so that one inch ball bearings can roll down the
deck and be projected backwards by the chute. The track should be about 6 feet
long so that the motion of the successive balls can be observed. If the system
starts from rest the first ball will go backwards, but the last ball will move in
the direction of the recoiling cart if the cart is sufficiently light.

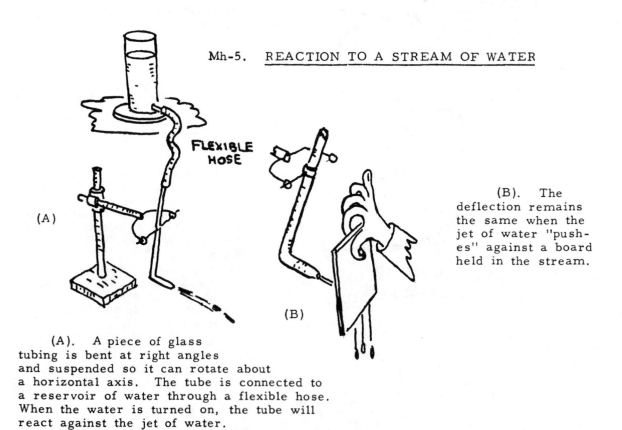

Mh-5. REACTION TO A STREAM OF WATER

FLEXIBLE
HOSE

(A)

(B)

(B). The
deflection remains
the same when the
jet of water "push-
es" against a board
held in the stream.

(A). A piece of glass
tubing is bent at right angles
and suspended so it can rotate about
a horizontal axis. The tube is connected to
a reservoir of water through a flexible hose.
When the water is turned on, the tube will
react against the jet of water.

Mi-1. VELOCITY OF A SOFTBALL

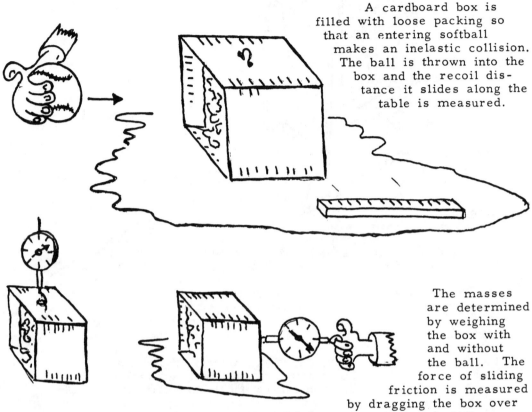

A cardboard box is filled with loose packing so that an entering softball makes an inelastic collision. The ball is thrown into the box and the recoil distance it slides along the table is measured.

The masses are determined by weighing the box with and without the ball. The force of sliding friction is measured by dragging the box over the same region. The acceleration is determined from the measured sliding force of friction and the mass. The velocity after the collision is determined from the relation between velocity, acceleration, and displacement.

Mi-2. RECOIL OF A CANNON

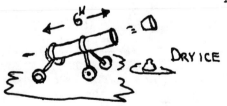

A one inch tube closed at one end is mounted on wheels as a cannon. A piece of dry ice is dropped into the cannon and firmly corked. When the cork blows out the cannon recoils.

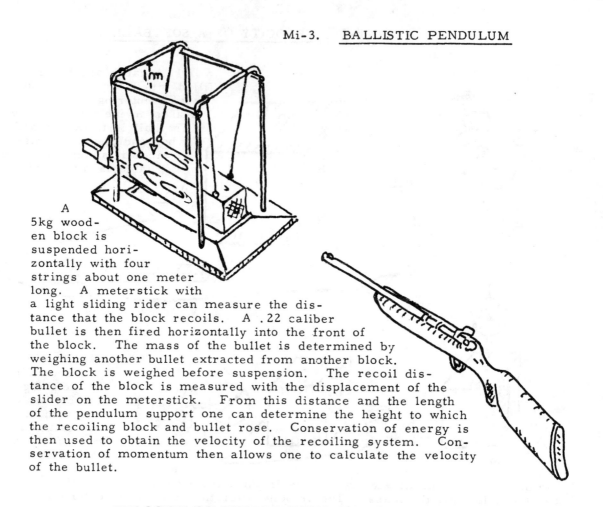

A 5kg wooden block is suspended horizontally with four strings about one meter long.   A meterstick with a light sliding rider can measure the distance that the block recoils.   A .22 caliber bullet is then fired horizontally into the front of the block.   The mass of the bullet is determined by weighing another bullet extracted from another block. The block is weighed before suspension.   The recoil distance of the block is measured with the displacement of the slider on the meterstick.   From this distance and the length of the pendulum support one can determine the height to which the recoiling block and bullet rose.   Conservation of energy is then used to obtain the velocity of the recoiling system.   Conservation of momentum then allows one to calculate the velocity of the bullet.

Mi-4.   VELOCITY OF BULLET USING THE AIR TRACK

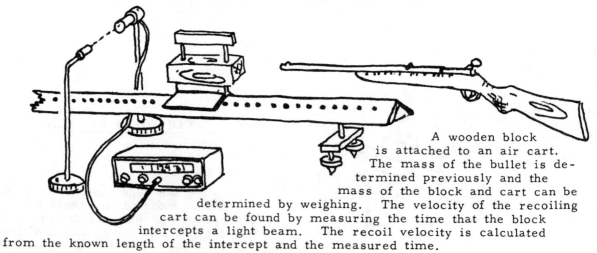

A wooden block is attached to an air cart. The mass of the bullet is determined previously and the mass of the block and cart can be determined by weighing.   The velocity of the recoiling cart can be found by measuring the time that the block intercepts a light beam.   The recoil velocity is calculated from the known length of the intercept and the measured time.

Mj-1. VECTOR SUM OF FORCES

Large dial type spring balances are attached to the top of the blackboard. A known weight is hung at various points on a string between them. In each case the vectors can easily be placed on the blackboard and equilibrium conditions worked out.

Mj-2. FORCES ON AN INCLINED PLANE

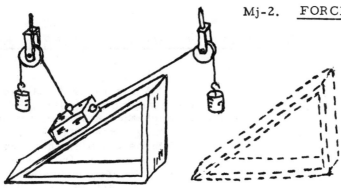

A cart or block is placed on an inclined plane and the tangential force maintained with a string, pulley, and weight. The normal force can then be calculated and applied with a second string, pulley, and weight. The inclined plane is then removed and the block remains suspended in space.

Mj-3. BREAKING WIRE

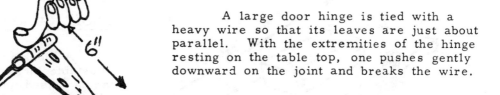

A large door hinge is tied with a heavy wire so that its leaves are just about parallel. With the extremities of the hinge resting on the table top, one pushes gently downward on the joint and breaks the wire.

Mk-1. FORCE OF FRICTION

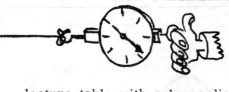

A wooden block having the shape of a rectangular parallelepiped is pulled across the lecture table with a large dial balance. The block may be turned on different edges to show the independence of frictional forces on area. A second block with various types of surfaces can be used to show the effects of different kinds of contact planes.

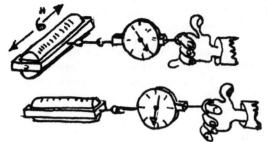

Mk-2.   ROLLING AND SLIDING
FRICTION

A cylindrical roller with a draw bar yoke may be pulled across the lecture table so that it can roll or slide.   The corresponding forces are read on a large dial balance.

Mk-3.   BRAKES ON FRONT AND REAR WHEELS

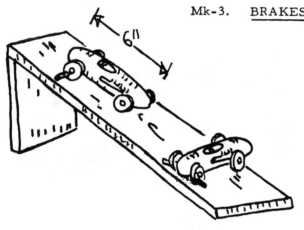

A toy racer is allowed to roll down an inclined plane.   A pin through the rear wheels produces a breaking force at the rear.   If the car turns a little, there will also be sliding of the front wheels which makes the motion unstable. When the brakes are on the front wheels, a slight turning of the car increases the torque due to sideways sliding of the back wheels which gives the car a righting moment and keeps it moving in a straight line.

Mk-4.   ANGLE OF REPOSE

A block is placed on an adjustable inclined plane which can be raised until the block slides with uniform velocity down the plane.   The tangent of the angle then gives the co-efficient of friction between these surfaces.   The difference between dynamic and static friction may also be demonstrated.

Ml-1.   TENSION IN A STRING

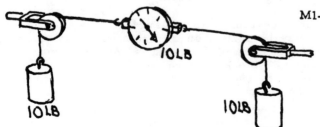

A spring balance is connected to strings which run over pulleys.   Equal weights are placed on the ends of the string.   The balance reads the value of one of the weights.

M1-2. BED OF NAILS

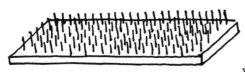

A 3 foot by 1.5 foot board has 16 penny nails pounded into it so the nails extend through the board. The nails are spaced at about 1 inch intervals. The instructor lies on the board while weights are gently piled onto him. It is more difficult to walk barefooted across the board.

Mm-1. CENTRIPETAL FORCE

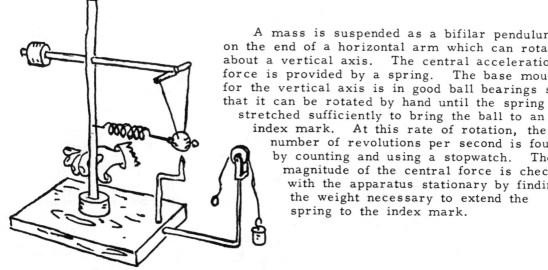

A mass is suspended as a bifilar pendulum on the end of a horizontal arm which can rotate about a vertical axis. The central acceleration force is provided by a spring. The base mount for the vertical axis is in good ball bearings so that it can be rotated by hand until the spring is stretched sufficiently to bring the ball to an index mark. At this rate of rotation, the number of revolutions per second is found by counting and using a stopwatch. The magnitude of the central force is checked with the apparatus stationary by finding the weight necessary to extend the spring to the index mark.

Mm-2. CENTRIPETAL FORCE

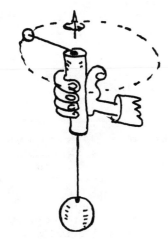

A small bead and large ball are on opposite ends of a string threaded through a lucite handle. Their unequal weights may be shown by holding the handle horizontally. If the bead is now whirled, it can easily raise the heavy ball. The effect of the equivalent force at various radii on angular velocities may be shown.

Mm-3. ROLLING CHAIN

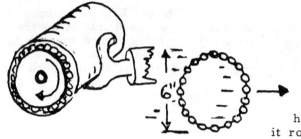

A very flexible endless chain is fitted onto a pulley on a high speed D.C. electric motor. When the motor is up to speed, it may be jerked sideways and thus release the chain which now has the form of a hoop. Its rapid motion will set it rolling across the lecture table and over many obstacles placed in its path.

Mm-4. CENTRIFUGE

(A). Some mercury and colored water are placed in a glass vessel which can be spun about its vertical axis of symmetry. The vessel is shaped with a variable radius so that on spinning the mercury forms a band at the greatest radius.

(B). Two flexible hoops can be spun about a common diametric axis. When rotated, the additional stresses set up to produce the necessary central forces cause the hoops to assume an elliptical shape with the minor axis along the axis of rotation. This is analogous to the flattening of the earth due to its rotation.

(C). The principle of the fly-ball governor can be shown by spinning a set of fly-balls to show how their position can be used to determine the setting of a throttle.

Mm-5. LOOP THE LOOP

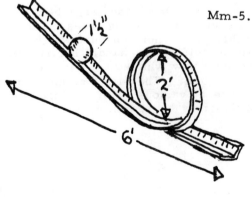

A piece of angle iron is shaped in the form of an inclined plane terminated in a vertical circular loop of radius R. A steel ball is then rolled in the trough of the angle iron. The theoretical height of the plane, 5/2 R, for the ball to complete the loop can be tested quite well.

Mm-6.   FRICTION AND TIPPING FORCES
              IN CENTRAL ACCELERATION

A motor driven turntable with
adjustable speed carries objects
which may slide or tip when the
table is rotated.

Mm-7.   HAND CRANKED
                 CENTRIFUGE

Test tube holders are
pivoted at the ends of a
horizontal bar which can
be made to rotate by hand
cranking. The angle of
the test tubes changes
with rotation rate. Such
substances as muddy
water may be placed in
the test tubes to show the
results of pressure grad-
ients due to the central
acceleration. These
results can easily be compared with those obtained
from gravitational pres-
sure gradients by not
turning the device.

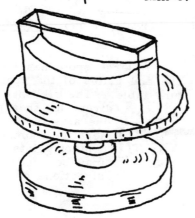

Mm-8.   EQUAL PRESSURE SURFACE

A flat sided tank is
placed onto a rotating
platform. The surface
of one atmosphere of
pressure is a parab-
oloid of revolution.

M-31

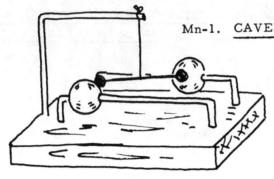

Mn-1.   CAVENDISH BALANCE

A model Cavendish balance is used for demonstration purposes.   Two small balls are constructed to form a torsion balance.   Two large balls slide along rails so that they can exchange interactions with the small balls.

Mo-1.   LOADED BEAM

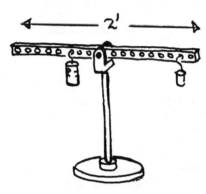

A simple horizontal bar pivoted on knife edges can be used to check equality of clockwise and counterclockwise moments.

Mo-2.   FORCE DISC

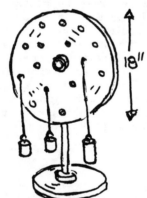

A vertical disc which is free to rotate contains many holes in which weights can be attached.   Equilibrium conditions for any combination of weights may be checked.   This apparatus shows nicely the importance of using perpendicular distances to the line of action of a force.

Mo-3.   MOMENTS

A large spool has ribbon wound on the axle. The end plates of the spool can roll on the lecture table.   The ribbon can be pulled in various directions in a plane perpendicular to the axis of the spool.   Positive or negative moments of force about the contact points between spool and table may be produced with corresponding directions of rotation.

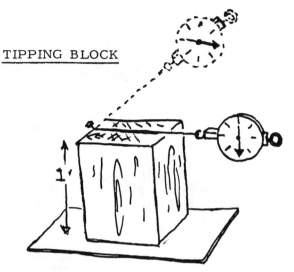

Mo-4. TIPPING BLOCK

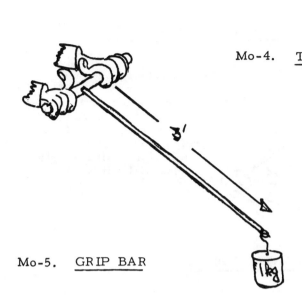

Mo-5. GRIP BAR

A large wooden block is placed
on a rough surface so that it will not
slide. A force is applied with a
spring balance, first parallel to the
horizontal along the top edge and
then perpendicular to a diagonal
drawn to the tipping axis where the
required force is less.

Various students may test
their grip strength by seeing how
close to horizontal they can bring
the 1 kg. weight.

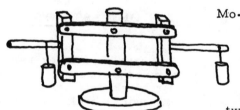

Mo-6. TORQUE INDEPENDENT OF
LEVER ARM

This is actually a model of
the platform balance. Equal
weights will balance no matter
where they are placed on the
two horizontal arms.

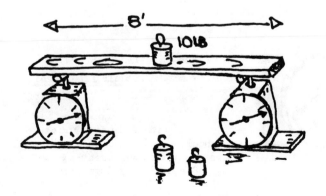

Mo-7. LOADED BEAM

Two spring platform bal-
ances carry a horizontal board
and weight. Many problems
in statics can be set up and
checked.

Mo-8. FORCES ON A LADDER

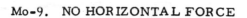

A small ladder is leaned against a vertical wall. The bottom end of the ladder is placed on either a smooth or rough (sandpaper) surface. A weight can be moved up the ladder to find when the ladder will slip.

Mo-9. NO HORIZONTAL FORCE

A stick has a swivel connection to a cork at one end and a string at the other. At equilibrium the string must be vertical.

Mp-1. CENTER OF MASS MOTION

A freely swinging pendulum with massive bobs is mounted on an air track cart. As the pendulum swings back and forth, the air cart recoils in such a way that the center of mass remains at rest.

Mp-2. DISCUS WITH SHIFTING CM

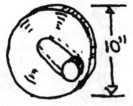

The light wooden disc is loaded with a heavy metal slug which can be shifted. The disc is then thrown spinning about its axis of symmetry into the air-once with the heavy slug at the center and then with the slug toward one edge. The trajectory of the center of mass is parabolic while the disc spins around the center of mass.

Mp-3. DISC ROLLING UPHILL

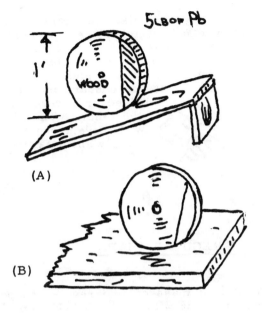

5 LB OF Pb

(A)

(B)

(A). A loaded disc is placed on an inclined plane so that it might roll down the plane. If the concealed loaded region is properly oriented so its minimum of potential energy lies up the plane, the disc will surprisingly roll up the plane.

(B). If the disc is released near the edge of the lecture bench, it will roll to the edge, stop before going off the edge, and then roll back.

Mp-4. BALANCING HORSE

A horse with an attached weight is constructed so that the center of mass of the system lies below the support point on the horse, and any motion about this point raises the center of mass of the horse. The horse will then precariously stand on various precipices.

Mp-5. BALANCING TWO FORKS AND MATCH WHILE EMPTYING GLASS

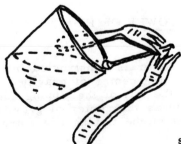

With a little practice the forks and match can be stuck together so the center of mass is below the head of the match. The head of the match is then placed on the rim of a glass full of water. The glass may then be emptied cautiously.

Mp-6.   UNICYCLE

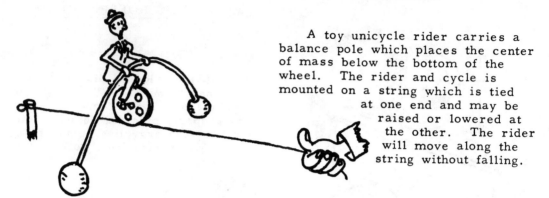

A toy unicycle rider carries a balance pole which places the center of mass below the bottom of the wheel.   The rider and cycle is mounted on a string which is tied at one end and may be raised or lowered at the other.   The rider will move along the string without falling.

Mp-7.   IRREGULAR SHAPE

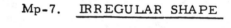

The center of mass of an irregular shape is found by supporting it with a plumb bob from various points.   The center of gravity fixed in the object always orients itself with minimum potential energy on a vertical line below the support point.

Mp-8.   EARTH-MOON SYSTEM

Two unequal masses are fastened to the end of a rigid bar.   Two bearing holes are drilled through the bar, one at the center of the bar and the other at the center of mass of the system.   By inserting the shaft and handle one can set the system into rotation by moving the shaft when the rotation is about the geometrical center, but not when the rotation is about the center of mass.

Mp-9.   LEANING TOWER OF PISA

A model of the tower is constructed in sections.   As long as the center of gravity lies on a vertical line to the left of the tipping edge, it is stable.   As soon as the center of gravity is shifted to the right of the tipping edge, the system becomes unstable.

Mp-10. ACROBAT

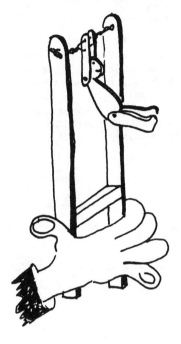

A twisted rubber band extends between two vertical supports. The band is strung through the arms of the jointed acrobat. The vertical supports are joined by a lower horizontal support and the frame is flexible at the junctions. When one squeezes the lower extended vertical members, the acrobat does amazing tricks.

Mp-11. SHIFTING CENTER OF GRAVITY

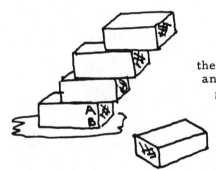

A set of blocks is stacked with their line of centers at some oblique angle. As soon as the center of gravity of the stack is to the right of "A", the stack tips about an axis through "A". One can discuss why the stack does not tip about an axis through "B" or any other axis.

Mp-12. CENTER OF GRAVITY OF A STOOL

A stool has been constructed which has a support point at its center of gravity. A blackboard pointer at this point will then support the stool oriented in any position.

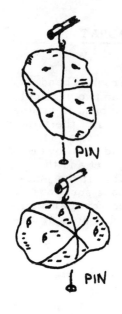

Mp-13. CENTER OF GRAVITY OF A POTATO

A string is tied around a potato so that it can be hung in several positions. While the potato is suspended a pin is stuck into it at the bottom along the support line. The potato is hung in several different positions and a pin is added in each position. All the pins point to the center of gravity.

PIN

PIN

Mp-14. TIPPING BLOCK ON INCLINE

A rectangular block is placed on a hinged incline. The incline is then raised until the center of mass of the block moves to the left of the lower edge of the block and the block tips.

Mp-15. WEIGHT OF A BROOM

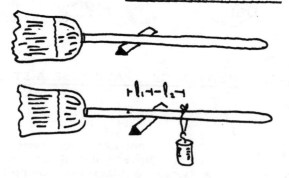

The position of the center of gravity of a broom is found by balancing it on a support. The point is then marked with tape or chalk. The system is rebalanced with a kilogram weight hanging on the handle. The distance from the new support to the center of gravity, ℓ_1, and the distance from the new support to the kilogram weight, ℓ_2, is measured. The weight of the broom is calculated by equating torques.

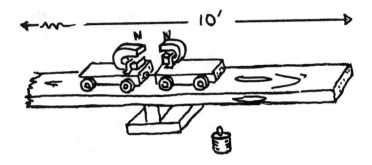

Mp-16.   SEE-SAW CENTER OF MASS

Two roller skate carts have large Alnico magnets mounted on them with polarities such the magnets repel each other.   The two carts are placed on a plank which has been balanced over a fulcrum.   The carts are tied together with a string and the entire system is balanced on the fulcrum.   When the string is burned, the carts recoil but the system remains in balance until a cart rolls off the end.   The carts may be loaded in different ways.

Mp-17.   MOTION OF
             CENTER OF MASS

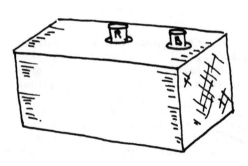

A wooden block has two holes drilled through it so that large felt pens can be inserted. One hole passes through the center of mass of the block and the other is to one side. The block is then placed on a large sheet of paper and given a sharp off center blow with a hammer. The pen trace connected with the center of mass will be a straight line while the other trace will move about this line.

Mp-18.   MOTION OF CENTER OF MASS ON AIR TABLE

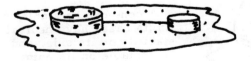

Pucks of different masses are tied together by a string and started with a spinning motion on the air table.   The center of mass shows only rectilinear motion.

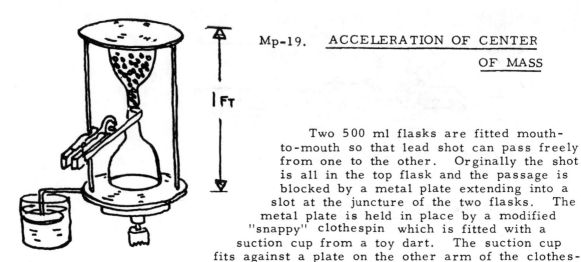

Mp-19.   ACCELERATION OF CENTER
                              OF MASS

Two 500 ml flasks are fitted mouth-to-mouth so that lead shot can pass freely from one to the other. Orginally the shot is all in the top flask and the passage is blocked by a metal plate extending into a slot at the juncture of the two flasks.   The metal plate is held in place by a modified "snappy" clothespin which is fitted with a suction cup from a toy dart.   The suction cup fits against a plate on the other arm of the clothespin and holds it compressed until air leaks in and lets the arms of the clothespin separate.   This separation pulls the plate between the two flasks out of the passage and allows the shot to fall into the lower flask.   The entire system is placed on a balance with an oil filled dashpot to prevent excessive motion.   The flask system moves upward at the instant of opening when the center of mass is accelerated downward.   There is no deflection while the lead shot is dropping at a uniform rate.   Finally there is a downward deflection when the center of mass is decelerated as the last lead shot leaves the upper flask.

Mq-1.   STABILITY

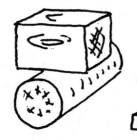

A rectangular block is balanced on a cylinder. If the distance between the base of the block and its center of gravity is less than the radius of the cylinder, the system is stable and the block will balance. If the distance from the base of the block to the center of gravity is greater than the radius of curvature, the system is unstable.

Mq-2.   STABILITY OF CONE AND SPHERE

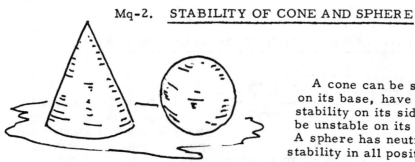

A cone can be stable on its base, have neutral stability on its side, and be unstable on its point. A sphere has neutral stability in all positions.

Mr-1. ROLLING UP HILL

A "V" shaped wooden rail system is supported so that the open end of the "V" is higher than the closed end. A double cone is cut at an angle so that as the cone rolls on the rails its center of mass is lowered. The cone will roll up hill **if** the center of mass is lowered faster than the rail system can raise it.

Mr-2. CONSERVATION OF ENERGY

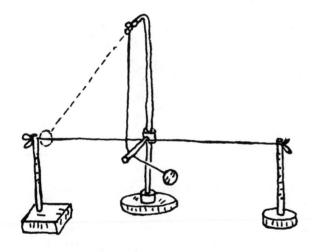

A piece of angle iron is bent so that it forms two inclined planes of different slope. A steel ball rolled down one plane will roll up the other to the same height.

Mr-3. STOPPED PENDULUM

A pendulum is set swinging and the highest points of the arc are marked with a horizontal string. A stop is then inserted which changes the arc along which the bob travels. The bob still returns to the height of the horizontal string.

Mr-4. ROLLING SPOOL

A spool with large end plates is rolled down an inclined plane on the small axle. When the end plates come in contact with the horizontal tabletop, the spool takes off with a much higher linear velocity across the tabletop.

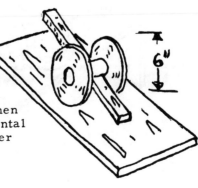

Mr-5. ANGULAR MOTION

Two heavy weights are attached to a bar which can rotate about a horizontal axis. The system is driven by a string wrapped around an attached wheel and connected to a falling weight. There is then exchange of energy between the potential energy of the weight and kinetic energy of rotation.

Mr-6. LARGE PENDULUM

A very heavy pendulum bob is supported from the ceiling on a vertical line about 6 feet from the blackboard. The instructor then places the back of his head against the board and the bob at the tip of his nose. He releases the bob from rest (with no initial velocity) and patiently awaits the return of the bob to the tip of his nose.

Ms-1. RACING DISCS

Two wooden discs with identical mass, shape, and size are loaded with lead so they have quite different moments of inertia about their axes of symmetry. When the discs are rolled down an inclined plane, the disc with the smaller moment of inertia always wins the race down the plane.

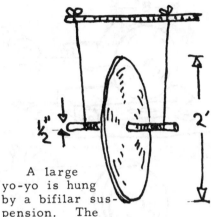

Ms-3. RACING ROTATORS

Rings, discs, and spheres of various sizes and shapes are rolled down an inclined plane. The object with the smallest second geometric moment will always win.

A large yo-yo is hung by a bifilar suspension. The string unwinds from the axle and converts the gravitational potential energy to kinetic energy of rotation and a very little translational energy. When the yo-yo reaches the bottom, the string rewinds and allows the kinetic energy to be restored as potential energy.

Ms-4. MOMENTS OF INERTIA

Circular aluminum plates are joined together by heavy brass cylinders. The end plates are drilled so that the cylinders may be close to the axis or close to the periphery. The relative values of the moments of inertia are tested by having the objects race rolling down an inclined plane. The object having the smaller moment of inertia always wins the race.

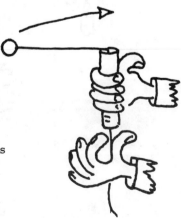

Ms-5. WHIRLAGIG

The apparatus is the same as Mm-2. The ball is set whirling, and the angular velocity is changed by lengthening or shortening the supporting string.

Ms-6.   FORCE BETWEEN SURFACE AND
                    ROLLING OBJECT

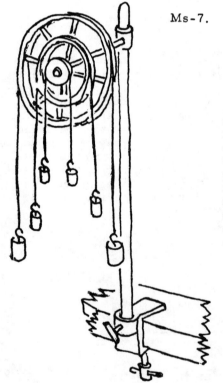

A 5 pound, 8" diameter pulley
is built so that it may be drawn horizontally by a force applied at the
axis of symmetry or by a string
wound around its periphery.   The pulley is then placed on a freely moving
roller skate cart.   When the pulley
is accelerated by a force on its axis,
the roller skate cart moves forward
showing that the force on the pulley
was backward.   When the pulley is
accelerated by the string around its periphery, the roller skate moves backward showing
that the contact force on the pulley was forward.

Ms-7.   LINEAR AND ANGULAR DYNAMICS

A skeletonized aluminum pulley with
good bearings can carry strings connecting equal weights over various diameter sections of the pulley.   A small
added weight may be placed on any of
the other weights.   The linear and angular accelerations of the various weights
may be determined.   The concept of
moment of inertia can be derived by
showing that the weights could be fastened directly to the wheel and produce the
same result.

Mt-1. ANGULAR MOMENTUM

A flyball governor can be expanded or contracted by a system of levers. If given some angular momentum in the expanded position, it will run much more rapidly on contraction. The changes are sufficiently great so that almost undetectable motion in the expanded position becomes quite rapid in the contracted position.

Mt-2. BALLET DANCER WITH DUMBBELLS

A freely rotating platform carries the instructor with a heavy dumbbell in each hand. When given a small amount of angular momentum, the instructor can vary his angular velocity at will by changing the radius at which he supports the dumbbells.

Mt-3. BASEBALL PLAYER

The instructor stands on the freely rotating platform with a baseball bat. Swinging the bat results in the batter recoiling with the opposite angular velocity.

Mt-4. ANGULAR MOMENTUM OF A TRAIN

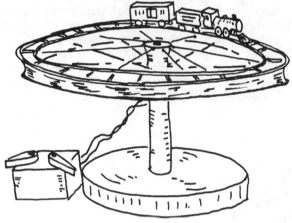

Track for a toy electric train is mounted on the periphery of a freely rotating horizontal bicycle wheel. Slip rings must be made to transfer power to the track. When the train starts to move around the track, the bicycle wheel and track move in the opposite direction.

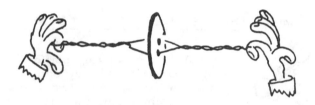

Mt-5. BUZZ BUTTON

A large button is threaded onto a loop of string. The button is then rotated to twist the string. One then pulls on the string and the torque due to tension in the twisted string sets the button into rotation. The inertia of the button winds the string in the opposite direction so the system can be made to oscillate.

Mt-6. LAWN SPRINKLER

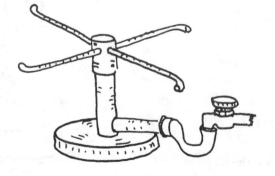

A lawn sprinkler is run to show how the reaction to the exiting water yields a torque which turns the sprinkler.

Mt-7. <u>IMPACT PARAMETER</u>

The instructor sits on a stool
which in turn is on a rotating platform.
A student can throw to the instructor
a bag of lead shot directed off the
axis of the rotating system. When
the instructor catches the bag, he
will rotate. The instructor may also
throw the shot bag with a sidearm
throw to change his angular
momentum.

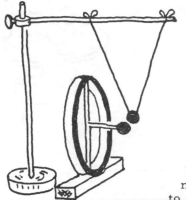

Mt-8. <u>TRANSFER OF</u>
<u>ANGULAR MOMENTUM</u>

A ball is suspended so it is free
to turn inside a gimbal support in a
horizontal circle. A bifilar pendulum
sits to one side and is adjusted so
that the pendulum ball can strike the
ball in the gimbal. The balls have equal
mass. The pendulum ball is then swung
to hit the gimbal supported ball which is
initially at rest. The pendulum stops in an
elastic collision while the gimbal ball rotates
once in a horizontal circle. It then strikes the pendulum ball on
the back side and the pendulum completes its swing.

Mu-1. BICYCLE WHEEL

This experiment is used to demonstrate conservation of angular momentum about a vertical axis. A bicycle wheel is mounted on good bearings so that it spins about its axis. The instructor stands on the rotating platform with the bicycle wheel turning. (A spin of the wheel with the hand gives a sufficient velocity.) The instructor then turns the wheel over and receives an angular velocity in the opposite direction. The instructor can then pass the wheel to some stationary helper who re-inverts it and gives it back to the instructor who can invert it again, etc., etc..

Mu-2. PRECESSION OF GYRO

A bicycle wheel is mounted to spin about a horizontal axis. The wheel is counterbalanced by a weight on the other end on the axle and the whole system can precess about a vertical axis. A gravitational torque can be applied by moving the counterbalance. The direction of this torque should be tested with the wheel at rest. Now with the wheel spinning in either direction, the laws of precession may be tested.

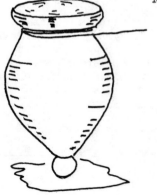

Mu-3. OLD FASHIONED TOP

An old fashioned top is spun by throwing the top with a string wrapped around the periphery. This top, with its broad tip, will allow frictional torques to align the angular momentum vector along the axis of symmetry so that the top will "sleep".

M-48

Mu-4. GYRO IN A SUITCASE

   A large gyro is mounted in a suitcase.
Students are then asked to carry the suitcase. It is best to have this brought in
about 10 minutes from the end of the period
so students can come up after class and
try the experiment themselves.

Mu-5. SPIN AND ROTATION

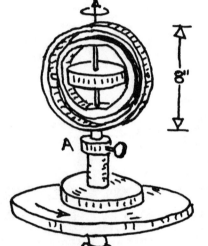

   A gyroscope with gimbals which allow
rotation about three axes is brought to speed
and placed on a turntable.   The angular momentum vector of the gyroscope remains fixed
in space as the turntable is rotated.   Then the
degree of freedom about the vertical axis is
removed by tightening the setscrew at A.   If
the turntable is rotated, the angular momentum
vector of the gyroscope will align with the angular velocity vector of the turntable.   If the
direction of rotation of the turntable is reversed,
the gyroscope will flip over and become parallel
to the reversed angular velocity.   The gyroscope knows which way the turntable rotates.

Mu-6. INSTANTANEOUS AXIS

   The bicycle wheel is pivoted at the center of
mass so no gravitational torque can be applied.
A piece of printed paper is attached to the top
plate to show the position of the instantaneous
axis.   Since there is no motion at the instantaneous axis, the print at the axis can be discerned.
The motion of the instantaneous axis can be made
most clear by starting the system with the instantaneous axis along the axis of symmetry.   Then
the spinning wheel is given an angular impulse at
right angles to the original angular momentum in order to change the direction of the angular momentum.
The magnitude of the angular momentum remains con-
stant, but its direction is different from that of the instantaneous axis, so the
instantaneous axis moves around the printed page.

Mu-7.   PRECESSING TOP

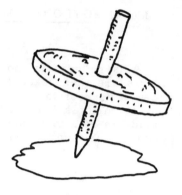

A 6 inch aluminum disc which is 3/8 inch thick is made into a top with a sharp point. With a simple hand spin it is easy to get the angular momentum vector on the axis of symmetry. The top then precesses under a gravitational torque.

Mu-8.   FEEL OF A GYROSCOPE

A heavy gryoscope wheel is set to spinning by a rubber friction disc on an auxiliary motor. Handles extend from the gimbal ring so that one can hold the gyro. If one places a torque on the gyroscope normal to the spin axis, the gyro tends to move so that the spin vector chases the torque vector.

Mu-9.   BICYCLE EFFECTS

A bicycle wheel is mounted in the front fork of a bicycle. The wheel is given a hand spin. In order to make the wheel turn in the fork bearing one tips the device. One "tips the bicycle the way one wants to turn the bicycle".

Mu-10. **MITAC GYROSCOPE**

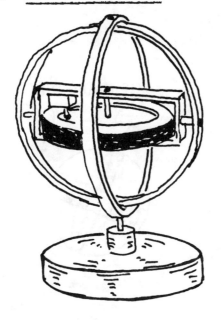

This is a commercially built gyroscope. Power to a small friction drive motor that drives the gyro wheel is carried by wires through the many gimbal joints. Projections extend from the central yoke so that weights can be added to place gravitational torques on the wheel. The various gimbal joints may be locked at will in order to study how the gyroscope reacts to the loss of degrees of freedom. The reaction torques to applied torques can be shown when the gimbals are locked. Most of the other gyroscope experiments can be performed with this device and the gyro wheel will not slow down due to frictional forces.

Mu-11. **BALANCING LADDER**

A gyroscope in its gimbal has a second gimbal in the form of ladder rungs. The vertical axis through the ladder rung holds a crank attached to a spring. The crank and spring are oriented in an unstable position. The system as it stands is unstable to gravitational torques. There are then two unstable coordinates for the gyro. The system will become stable when the gyro is set in motion and the ladder will not tip.

Mu-12. AIR SUSPENDED GYROSCOPE

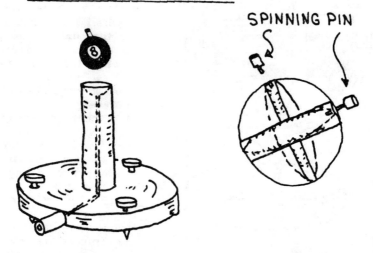

SPINNING PIN

The gyroscope is a billiard ball which can rest it a spherical cavity at the top of a vertical post. Air fed through the post suspends the ball so that it can turn almost free of friction. The ball is spun by hand by means of a pin twister which can be left in the ball or removed. If the pin is left in the ball, there will be a gravitational torque on the ball and it will precess. A special ball is constructed with brass rods of different sizes along orthogonal axes so that the ellipsoid of inertia is truly an ellipsoid. As Mu-20 shows, the rotation is most stable about an axis with maximum or minimum moments of inertia. If the spin of the ball is started about the intermediate axis, the ball will flip to the more stable spin. For more details see W. Harter, C.C. Kim, AJP 44, 1080 (1976).

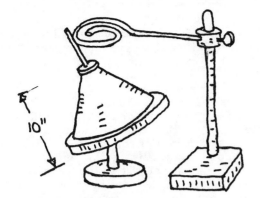

Mu-13.   MAXWELL'S GYRO

The gyro is pivoted at its center of mass. The extended upper shaft can then be brought into contact with a wire bent in some complex physical line lying in a horizontal plane. The frictional forces produce a torque which makes the gyro precess in such a manner that the normal force between the extended shaft and the wire is increased. The shaft then rolls along the complex contour of the wire.

Mu-14.   SPIN FLIPPING

A bicycle wheel is mounted at the end of a rod, and the system is held by a string at the other end of the rod. Due to the gravitational torque, the wheel will precess about a vertical axis when it is spinning. The instructor then places an additional torque on the system by trying to force the precession around the vertical axis. When he does this (with some practice) the angular momentum of the wheel will align itself with the applied torque, i.e., the gyroscope will rise to a vertical position.

Mu-15.   GYROSCOPE ON A TRAPEZE

A gyroscope from a surplus gyrocompass is placed on the top of a trapeze bar. The trapeze must have a degree of freedom about the axis of the bar, so bearings are used where the strings are attached. The second degree of freedom is about a vertical axis by having the bifilar suspension twisted a half turn, with one string passing through a ring in the other. The system is then statically unstable in a pair of coordinates, the horizontal bar axis and the vertical axis. Adding the gyroscope with spin makes the system dynamically stable.

Mu-16. MONORAIL CAR

A gyroscope is mounted on a two wheel cart which can ride a stretched wire or rail. The gyroscope wheel is horizontal so that the angular momentum is vertical. The gimbals have a degree of freedom about the horizontal axis normal to the stretched wire. As the system tips about an axis parallel to the wire, the angular momentum vector precesses to become aligned with the torque vector. This precession makes the mass M produce an additional torque parallel to the original precession vector. The angular momentum vector then tries to align with this new torque vector. The new precession due to the second torque opposes the original tipping motion and rights the cart. Two statically unstable degrees of freedom become stable.

Mu-17.   TIPPY-TOP

The top is constructed so that when it rests on the table its center of gravity is below the center of curvature of the surface of the top. The system is then statically stable. When given a rapid spin the top will flip and spin on the stem so that it has become statically unstable. Adding spin makes the statically unstable position become stable. It is important to notice that the angular momentum vector does not flip. The surface must be slightly rough so that frictional torques can be realized between the top and the table.

Mu-18.   SPINNING FOOTBALL

A football at rest on a table will be statically stable when it is laying on the surface with the greatest radius of curvature, the condition being that the center of gravity is below the center of curvature of the contact surface. When given a rapid spin, the football rises to its pointed end and finds dynamic stability with the center of gravity above the center of curvature of the pointed end. Spin makes a statically unstable position become dynamically stable.

Mu-19. FLIPPING IRON SLUG

← 2" →

A soft iron slug is cut into approximately the shape
of a football. It is placed in a watch glass which has
been waxed to the top of a magnetic chemical stirrer.
As the rotating magnet in the stirrer turns, it drags
the slug along. At slow speeds the slug is stable on
its side with the greatest radius of curvature. At a
critical speed of rotation the slug will flip and spin
on its pointed end. The spin makes the statically
unstable position become dynamically stable.

Mu-20. ROTATIONAL STABILITY

← 6" →

A piece of board with unequal length,
height, and width can be tossed into the
air spinning about various axes. When it is
spinning with a maximum or minimum moment
of inertia, the spinning is quite stable. If it is
spinning with some intermediate moment of inertia, the
spinning is unstable or wobbly.

10"

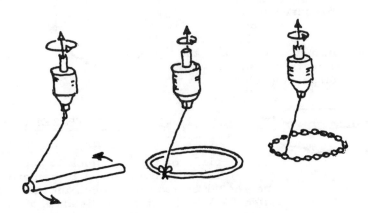

Mu-21. SPINNING LARIET

A rod, hoop, and endless chain can in turn be fastened
onto a hand drill chuck through a flexible wire. On spinning,
all objects assume an orientation which gives them a maximum
symmetrical moment of inertia about the axis of spin.

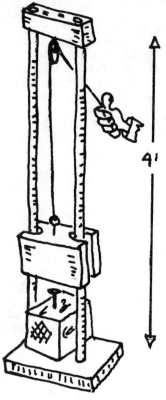

Mv-1. PILE DRIVER

A 10 pound block is guided between two vertical rails. Work is done on the system to raise the block. When the block falls, it gains kinetic energy. The energy is used to place a very large force on a nail through a short distance.

Mv-2. POWER

A belt is strung under tension around a large pulley which can be turned by the student. The frictional forces can be determined from the difference in the readings of the two spring balances when the pulley is turned. The distance is measured by counting the number of turns of the known diameter wheel and the time is measured with a large stop clock.

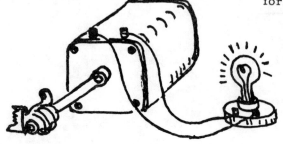

Mv-3. WORK TO REMOVE
TAPE

A piece of tape is stuck to the lecture bench. The maximum force to remove the tape should be expended when the tape is pulled back along itself a distance of twice the length. The assumption is made that the force to remove the tape is constant.

Mv-4. GENERATOR AND LIGHT
BULB

A 120 volt hand generator is used to light ordinary light bulbs. The class seems to appreciate 2¢ of electricity a little more after this experiment.

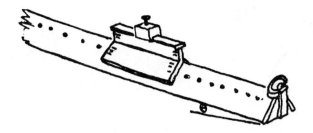

Mw-1. LOSS OF ENERGY

An air track is inclined at a small angle with respect to the horizontal. A good spring bumper is placed at the lower end. The cart carries a small weight that may be clamped tightly so it stays in place, or the weight may be loosened slightly so that it can slide a little during the collision with the spring bumper. The bounce is compared for the case of the tight clamp and the loose clamp, showing how energy can be lost internally in the cart.

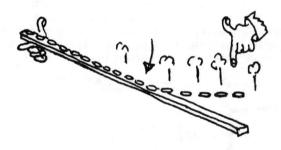

Mw-2. FALLING STICK WITH PENNIES

A meterstick is loaded uniformly with pennies and held horizontally. One end of the stick is released. Two-thirds of the pennies remain with the stick, but the last one-third break away and fall in a horizontal straight line.

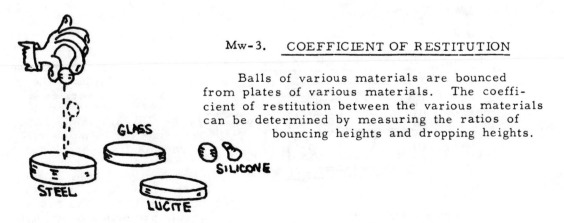

Mw-3. COEFFICIENT OF RESTITUTION

Balls of various materials are bounced from plates of various materials. The coefficient of restitution between the various materials can be determined by measuring the ratios of bouncing heights and dropping heights.

Mw-4. COLLISION TIME PENDULUM

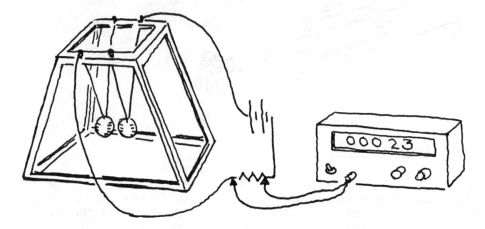

Two metal wire bifilar pendula are suspended in a frame
with the top member made of insulating material. The pendula
complete an electric circuit when they are in contact. When
the pendula collide, the duration of the collision can be measured
with a commercial timer. It is an interesting observation that
the harder the collision, the shorter the duration of the contact.

Mx-1. SIMPLE HARMONIC MOTION

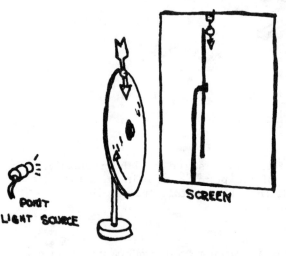

POINT
LIGHT SOURCE

SCREEN

A rotatable disc has a large arrow on its periphery. This can be
projected onto the wall with a point
source lamp. The arrow on the disc
can be oriented tangentially or radially,
and one can demonstrate nicely the
phase relations between displacement,
velocity, and acceleration, showing
how these quantities are related to the
corresponding quantities in uniform
circular motion.

Mx-2. PROJECTION MODEL OF SHM

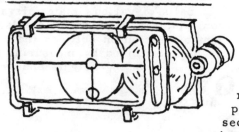

A motor drives two
geared wheels. The
first wheel carries a
Scotch yoke to give
rectilinear simple harmonic motion. The second
gear is transparent and
runs in a race around its
periphery. A spot on the
second gear shows uniform
circular motion. The two
spots show simple harmonic motion as the projection of uniform
circular motion when viewed using a projector.

Mx-3. MASS ON A SPRING

One can measure the force constant cf a spring and then measure the frequency for this type of oscillator. One can try different springs on masses and springs in series and in parallel. The problem of energy should be considered.

Mx-4. FORCE AND DISPLACEMENT

Small springs and masses are hung from a strain gauge which measures the force at the support point. The signal from the strain gauge is amplified and displayed on an oscilloscope. The oscillating masses can be hung close to the face of the oscilloscope so that students can observe the force and the displacement simultaneously. With separate tests one can show that the force is proportional to the negative of the displacement. One can show the relation of the frequency to the spring constant or to the mass, when the system is set into oscillation.

OSCILLOSCOPE

Mx-5. DRUNKEN SAILOR

A used soap bottle in the form of a man is suspended between two springs. The bottom of the lower spring is fastened by a string to a scotch yoke which in turn is driven by a variable speed motor. The frequency of the driving force is such that the system is in resonance when the man is half full of water. The man is then emptied without changing the frequency of the driving force. This takes the system far from resonance and the amplitude of oscillation is quite small. Water is then added from a wine bottle until resonance is reached and the man jumps wildly around. One continues to add water from the coffee pot, and the resonant frequency shifts to lower values so again the amplitude of oscillation is small.

Mx-6. CLOCKSPRING PENDULUM

A piece of clock spring is mounted on a heavy base. A mass, whose position on the spring can be altered, is set at different points to change the period of vibration.

Mx-7. AIR CART MASS AND SPRING

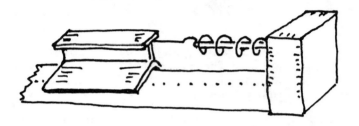

A horizontal mass and spring may be studied without the gravitational complication present in a vertically suspended system.

Mx-8. GRAPHICAL DISPLAY OF MECHANICAL RESONANCE

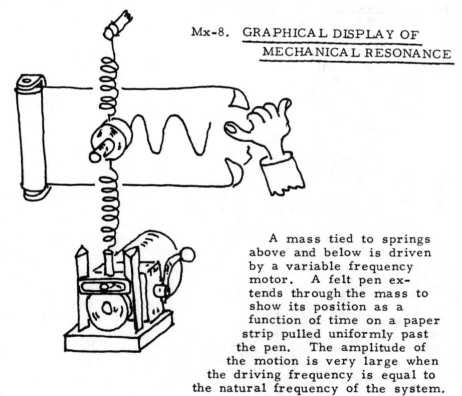

A mass tied to springs above and below is driven by a variable frequency motor. A felt pen extends through the mass to show its position as a function of time on a paper strip pulled uniformly past the pen. The amplitude of the motion is very large when the driving frequency is equal to the natural frequency of the system.

Mx-9.   DAMPED PENDULUM

An ordinary mass and spring oscillator has an attached dash pot.   Either oil or water may be used for a damping fluid.

Mx-10.   ADJUSTABLE COUPLED PENDULUM

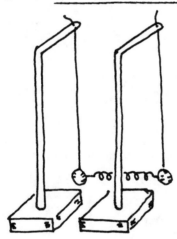

Pendulum stands are made, each having a hole at the support point so that the length of the pendulum may be easily changed.   Coupling between the pendula is realized by a very fine wire spring of many turns.   The coupling effects may then be studied as a function of the frequencies of the pendula.

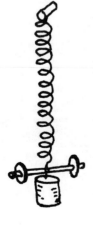

Mx-11.   WILBURFORCE PENDULUM

This pendulum has three modes of oscillation; simple pendulum, mass on a spring, and torsion pendulum.   The periods of all three modes are different, but are close to each other.   When the pendulum is set into motion, the system will pass cyclically from one mode to the next.

Mx-12. COUPLED PENDULUMS

Three identical pendulums are hung on a support which is slightly flexible. One pendulum is started and energy is slowly passed to the others. The energy transfer will go through several cycles.

Mx-13. RESONANCE REEDS

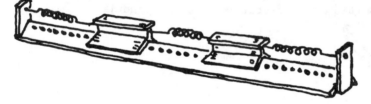

A set of steel reeds is mounted on a common strip as is found in speed indicators. Each reed has a slightly higher frequency than its right-hand neighbor in the mounting sequence. When the system is in contact with a vibrating device, the reed having the frequency closest to that of the device will have a maximum amplitude. If the system is viewed with a strobotac, one can observe the leading and lagging phase angles of the reeds with higher and lower frequencies which are partially in resonance.

Mx-14. COUPLED OSCILLATORS

Springs are placed between the air track carts and to the ends of the track. One then shows different modes of motion. A high frequency is realized when the air carts move in opposition, and a lower frequency when they move with parallel velocities.

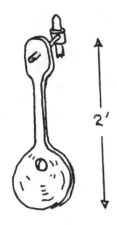

My-1.   REVERSIBLE PENDULUM

Suspension holes are drilled through an odd shaped board at a pair of conjugate points which make the physical pendulum have equal periods. The center of mass point can be determined by simple balancing over a straight edge, so one can proceed to determine the moment of inertia of this object about the center of mass and then any point.

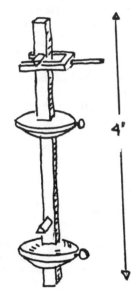

My-2.   KATER'S PENDULUM

This is an elaborately built pendulum which can be used to give a very good determination of g. The instructor should thoroughly review what adjustments he wants to make if he plans to do this measurement in class.

My-3.   OSCILLATING RING

A ring is placed on a knife edge at a point on its periphery so it can swing as a physical pendulum in its plane. A simple pendulum whose length is equal to the diameter of the ring is suspended beside it so the equality of periods can be observed.

My-4.   CENTER OF PERCUSSION AND CENTER OF OSCILLATION

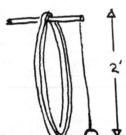

A rectangular bar is supported as a physical pendulum so that its pivot point can slide along two horizontal rails. The center of percussion is marked with a second support pin. A simple pendulum is supported from the fixed support point with its length equal to the distance between the two support points on the bar. The realations between the center of oscillation and the center of percussion can be both calculated and demonstrated.

My-5. CENTER OF PERCUSSION

A rectangular bar is suspended by a thread. Its center of percussion can be found by adjusting a simple pendulum to the same period and noting this length. When the bar is struck at the center of percussion it flies out and oscillates parallel to the thread. When struck above or below the center of percussion, the bar oscillates wildly with respect to the thread.

My-6. FALLING CHIMNEY

A hinged inclined plane has a niche at its highest point to support a ball. A few inches lower on the plane a can is attached. The plane is raised to an angle so that the ball is directly over the point occupied by the can when the plane is horizontal. When the tilted plane is released, the ball support and can suffers an acceleration greater than g and breaks away from the ball, arriving at the horizontal position in time to catch the more slowly falling ball. The ball appears to jump into the can.

My-7. BASEBALL BAT

A regular baseball bat is suspended as a physical pendulum so that its pivot point can slide along two horizontal rails. The position of the pivot point is indicated by an arrow. The center of percussion is marked on the bat. When the bat is struck above or below the center of percussion, the motion of the pivot point is as indicated by the arrow. When the bat is struck at the center of percussion, the pivot point does not move.

My-8. CORK PHYSICAL PENDULUM

A physical pendulum is constructed by attaching a cork to each end of a bent wire which is supported on a horizontal rod. The period of the pendulum is measured with the wire bent at different angles. One finds that the period is long when the angle of the bend is large and short when the angle is small, even though the moment of inertia of the pendulum is unchanged. Making the angle large raises the center of mass and effectively shortens the length of the pendulum.

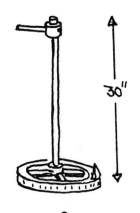

30"

Mz-1. TORSION PENDULUM

A wheel and flexible axle are suspended as a torsion pendulum. A more elaborate apparatus used in the laboratory allows one to calculate and measure directly the torsion constant of the rod and provides wheels with variable moments of inertia which can be readily calculated.

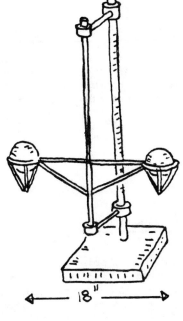

18"

Mz-2. INERTIA BALANCE

A light wire framework is built onto the end of a torsion rod. The framework can be loaded with various masses to show the dependence of period on moment of inertia or used as a device for comparing masses.

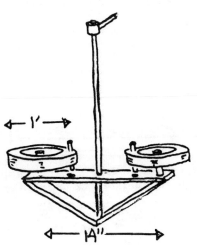

1'

14"

Mz-3. RIGID AND NON-RIGID MOTIONS

Two massive lead rings are mounted on a framework which can be suspended as a torsion pendulum. The rings can be locked or allowed to run free (i.e. rotate) on axes parallel to the torsion rod. The period is then measured with the rings locked and then with the rings free to show the significance of the terms in Steiner's equation for moments of inertia.

Mz-4.   OSCILLATING CHAIN

A chain is suspended from both ends by a string which runs over a pulley. A small rotation of the pulley then produces a restoring torque proportional to the displacement. This condition leads to simple harmonic motion.

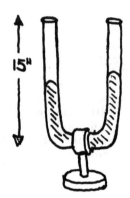

Mz-5.   OSCILLATING MERCURY COLUMN

An open "U" tube is partially filled with mercury. If the column is given a displacement, it will oscillate with simple harmonic motion similar to the chain in the previous demonstration.

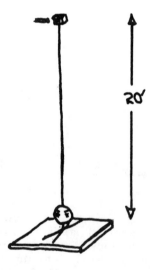

Mz-6.   FOUCAULT PENDULUM

A large simple pendulum has a point support on the ceiling. Its plane of motion is set and marked at the beginning of the class hour. The rotation of the index mark is then noted at the end of the hour. The amount of rotation gives a measure of the earth's angular velocity.

Mz-7.   MODEL OF FOUCAULT PENDULUM

A simple pendulum has a point support on a stand which is mounted on a turntable. The pendulum is put into oscillation in some plane. The plane of motion will then be maintained as the support stand is rotated in some arbitrary manner.

Mz-8. DYNAMIC STABILITY

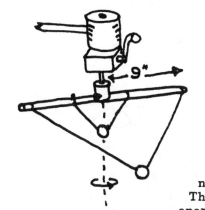

A variable speed motor is coupled to a horizontal rod so that the rod can be made to rotate in a horizontal plane with a variable rate. The rod holds bifilar pendula of different lengths. Initially all the pendula hang verticaly. As the system comes up to speed (slowly), the various pendula will assume a new stable position at an angle. The general idea is that the kinetic energy depends explicitly on a coordinate. New conditions for energy minima can then exist.

Mz-9. UPSIDE DOWN PENDULUM

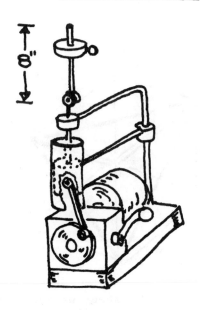

A variable speed motor yields vertical undulatory motion by means of a crankshaft and piston arrangement with good vertical guides. A rod and mass are then pivoted to form an inverted pendulum. At a respectably high frequency, the mass will oscillate stably in this inverted position. New conditions for an energy minimum develop because of the oscillatory motion.

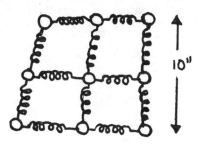

MA-1. CRYSTAL MODEL

Some plastic balls are connected by springs. The device may be strained to show the various geometric displacements of the molecules.

MA-2. CLOSE PACKED CRYSTALS

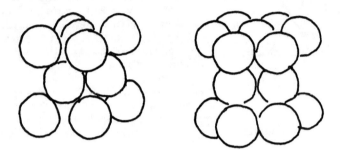

Old tennis balls are glued together to give two methods for forming close packed crystals.

MA-3. CRYSTAL STRUCTURE

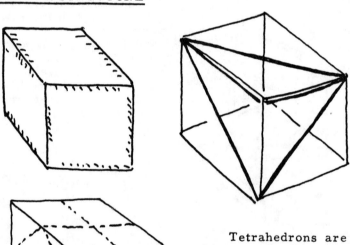

Tetrahedrons are made from a cube by sawing off corners. Octahedrons are made from a cube by sawing off triangular parallelepipeds parallel to all of the cube edges.

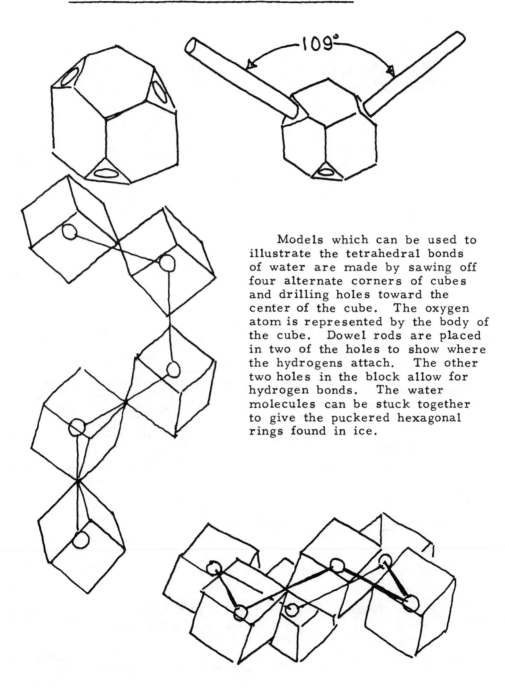

Models which can be used to illustrate the tetrahedral bonds of water are made by sawing off four alternate corners of cubes and drilling holes toward the center of the cube. The oxygen atom is represented by the body of the cube. Dowel rods are placed in two of the holes to show where the hydrogens attach. The other two holes in the block allow for hydrogen bonds. The water molecules can be stuck together to give the puckered hexagonal rings found in ice.

MA-5. FAULTS IN A CRYSTAL

Two flat pieces of clear plastic are cemented together with a separation such that small ball bearings may move freely between the sheets. The container is filled about 3/4 full of ball bearings and sealed. The ball bearings tend to form regular crystal-like arrays, but occasionally they become misaligned and a fault develops. One can show how the fault propagates by tapping the container.

MA-6. BOLOGNA BOTTLE

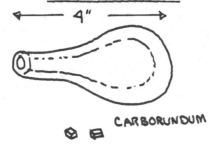

CARBORUNDUM

Bologna bottles are specialy built heavy walled bottles that contain a great amount of strain. One may pound on various objects very hard without breaking the bottle. A carborundum crystal placed in the bottle will scratch the surface and cause the bottle to shatter.

MA-7. CRUSHING A SALT CRYSTAL

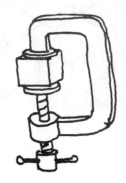

A large salt crystal can be placed into a "C" clamp and crushed in air. The breaks will occur along miniature faults in the crystal. If the system is placed under water, the faults heal, and it is very difficult to break the crystal.

MA-8.   SHEAR OF A BIG BOOK

A large book is placed on the table and pushed sideways to illustrate the geometry of shear deformations.

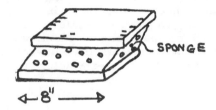

SPONGE

8"

MA-9.   SHEAR OF A SPONGE

This is essentially the same as the shear of a big book. It should be pointed out that these are not pure shears.

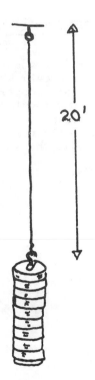

20'

MA-10.   ELASTIC LIMIT

A piece of bailing wire approximately 20 feet long is suspended from the ceiling with a weight pan on the lower end. Kilogram weights are added and the extension of the wire noted. Considerable suspense can be built up as one approaches the elastic limit.

MA-11. POISSON'S RATIO

A rubber hose is stretched and shows a lateral contraction as the length is increased.

MA-12. MODULUS OF RIGIDITY

A rod is clamped at one point on the lecture bench and the other end is attached to a wheel mounted on a bearing. Known torques may be applied to the rod by a string wrapped around the wheel. The twist in the rod is measured with an angular scale. The device is designed so that rods of identical geometry but of different materials may be compared. The rods are approximately 3/32" in diameter and 2 feet in length.

MA-13. BENDING AND TWISTING

A soft copper strip is wound onto a cylinder and the cylinder is then removed. If the copper coil is pulled straight, it will be twisted. The twist of the winding is proportional to the number of turns and the sine of the pitch angle.

FLUIDS

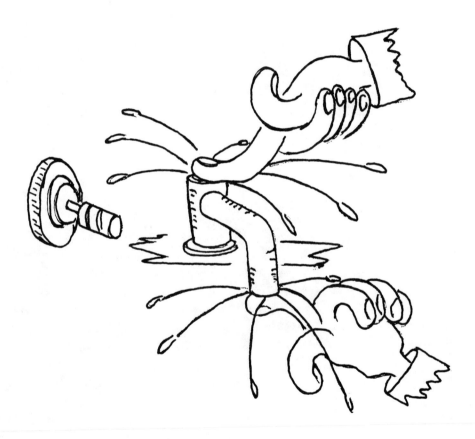

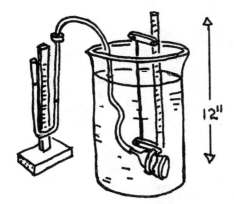

Fa-1. PRESSURE INDEPENDENT OF DIRECTION

Thistle tubes with rubber diaphrams are connected to manometers. One can show that the manometer reading depends only on the depth of the sensitive surface and not its orientation.

12"

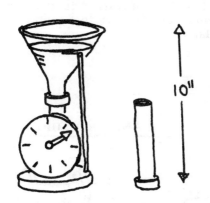

10"

Fa-2. PASCAL VASES

This is a commercial device with a dial type pressure gauge. One can demonstrate that the pressure depends on depth and not on the shape on the vessel.

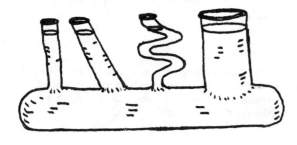

Fa-3. PASCAL VASES

A large glass container with several interconnecting open vertical tubes of different shapes shows the liquid rises to the same height in each.

Fa-4. WASSER WAGE

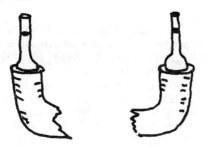

Two open tubes are connected with a long water filled hose. Points at the same height in the room may be determined. The device is useful for determining if foundations for buildings are level.

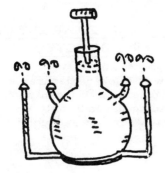

Fb-1. PASCAL FOUNTAIN

A metal container with jets emanating
from various points can have pressure applied
to a confined fluid by means of a piston.
Water squirts to the same height from all of
the jets.

Fb-2. PASCAL FOUNTAIN

This demonstration is the same as the
previous one except the container is made
of glass.

Fb-3. FORCE AND PRESSURE

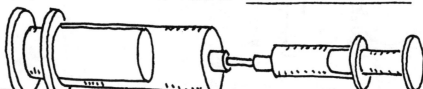

A large hypodermic syringe is joined to a small hypodermic
syringe. Both syringes are partially filled with water. Students
may test their relative strengths by pushing on the plungers.
The person on the smaller plunger can easily win.

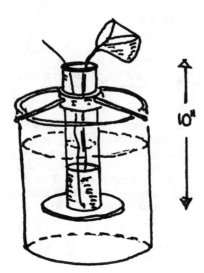

Fc-1. WATER PRESSURE

A cylindrical tube has a removable
bottom made in the form of a glass plate.
The glass plate is held in place by a string
as the cylinder with its removable bottom is
lowered into a tank of water. When it is
immersed, the water pressure in the tank
holds the bottom in place. Colored water
is then poured into the cylinder and the
bottom drops off when the level of the water
in the cylinder is approximately the same
as that in the tank.

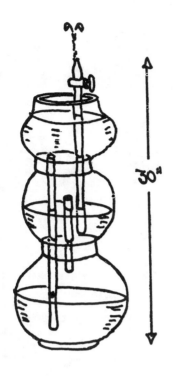

Fc-2.   HERO'S FOUNTAIN

This is a clever arrangement in which a column of water is balanced against a column composed of air and water sections. The geometric heights then can be quite different, and water seems to attempt to rise higher than a free surface in its reservoir.

Fd-1.   CRUSH CAN WITH PRESSURE

A one gallon can is evacuated with a forepump and is consequently crushed by the atmospheric pressure.

Fd-2.   MAGDEBURG HEMISPHERES

Two hemispheres are fit together with an airtight seal. After they are evacuated, they cannot be pulled apart by human forces.

Fd-3. WEIGHT OF BAROMETER

An empty barometer tube is weighed while
empty and then filled with mercury. The tube
is then inverted in a vat of mercury and the
barometer weighed again with a rather
surprising result.

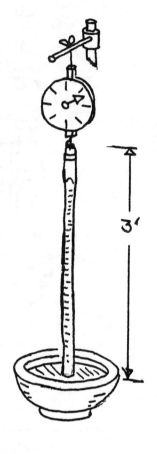

3'

Fd-4. LOW BAROMETRIC PRESSURE

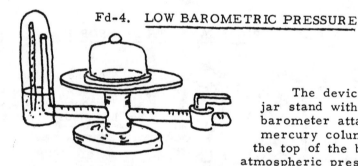

The device is a bell
jar stand with a 10 inch
barometer attached. The
mercury column is against
the top of the barometer at
atmospheric pressure. As
the air is pumped out of the bell
jar, the barometer will start reading when the pressure in the
bell jar falls below 10 inches of mercury.

Fe-1. ORDINARY SIPHON

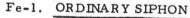

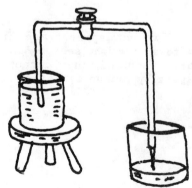

A glass tube filled with water
allows water to flow from a higher
to a lower level over a greater
intervening height.

F-6

Fe-2.   INTERMITTENT SIPHON

A funnel shaped vessel contains a exit opening through
a tube in the shape of a question mark.   As water is
poured into the funnel, nothing runs out until the water
level reaches the top of the question mark tube.   The
siphon is then self-starting and drains quickly to the level
of the open end of the tube.   If water is added continuously
and slowly, the process will repeat periodically showing the
nature of a relaxation oscillator.

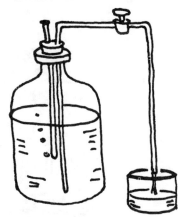

Fe-3. MARIOTTE FLASK
AND SIPHON

This form of the Mariotte
flask allows the siphon to flow with
a constant rate as the fluid level
changes.

Ff-1. BOURDON GAUGE

This is a large Bourdon gauge
left open so that its mechanism can
be observed.

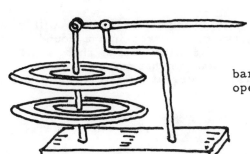

Ff-2.   ANEROID
BAROMETER

The operation of an aneroid
barometer is shown by this
open device.

Ff-3. CONSTANT HEIGHT OF A BAROMETER

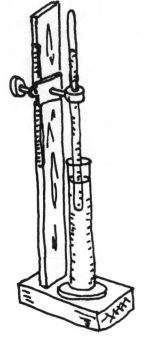

A mercury barometer is mounted so it can extend into a deep vat of mercury. The height of the mercury column remains constant as the barometer is moved up and down.

Fg-1. ARCHIMEDES' PRINCIPLE

A solid object which can fit snugly into a can is suspended below the can and the system weighed. The solid object is then immersed into the vessel which has been filled with water to an overflow pipe, with the corresponding loss in weight. The displaced water runs out the overflow pipe into another vessel. When this overflow water is added to the empty can, the original weight is restored.

Fg-2. BUOYANCY OF HOT AND COLD WATER

A hydrometer is made with a long glass tube corked into a round bottom flask. Sufficient lead shot is placed in the flask so that the hydrometer sinks in warm water and floats in cold water.

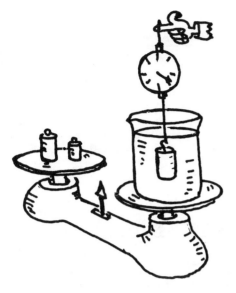

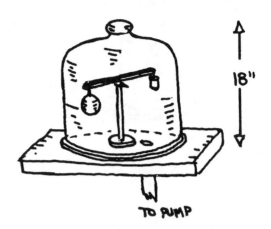

Fg-3. BUOYANCY OF AIR

Fg-4. LOSS OF WEIGHT IN WATER

A platform balance is balanced with a vessel of water. A solid object suspended from a dial balance is immersed into the water. The loss of weight on the dial balance equals the weight necessary to bring the platform back into balance.

A hollow sphere is balanced with a small volume weight in air. A bell jar is then placed on the system and pumped down. The hollow sphere appears to get heavier due to its greater loss of bouyant force.

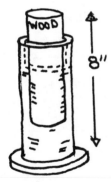

Fg-5. BATTLESHIP IN A CUP OF WATER

A wooden block with a rather large volume is shaped so that it just fits into a glass vessel. A few cubic centimeters of water is sufficient to float the block even though the displacement of the block is several times the volume of water.

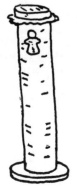

Fg-6. CARTESIAN DIVER

A small open ended vial is inverted into a larger vessel of confined water. The vial contains enough trapped air to just make it float. When the confined fluid is placed under pressure, the volume of the trapped air decreases and the diver sinks. On removing the pressure, the diver again rises.

Fg-7.   NICHOLSON BALANCE

This is a float which can be used with accurate
weights to make it float at an index mark on the stem.
The system can be balanced with an object on the submerged pan and on the top pan.   The methods of loss of
weight in water can then be applied to obtain the specific
gravity of the object on the submerged pan.

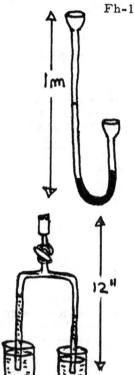

Fh-1.   COMPARISON OF FLUID DENSITIES

A "U" tube is partially filled with
mercury.   Other fluids can be poured
into the tube over the mercury and their
relative pressure heights compared.

Fh-2.   SPECIFIC GRAVITY OF LIQUIDS

Water and a liquid of unknown specific gravity can
be raised in vertical tubes by a common low pressure.
The densities of the liquids are inversely proportional
to the heights of the liquid columns.

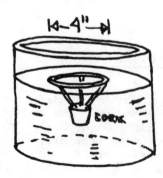

Fi-1.   SUBMERGED FLOAT

A large cork carries a light wire frame.
The cork and frame easily float on water.   The
whole system is then submerged with a section of
the wire frame against the surface.   The surface
tension holds the system submerged.

F-10

Fi-2.   WET MOP

A small mop is made up which is real fluffy
when dry. When the mop is wet, the surface
tension pulls the strands together into a rope-
like structure.

Fi-3.   SOAP BUBBLES

A "T" tube is used to blow up two soap bubbles of different sizes. The bubbles are then connected together, and the smaller bubble blows up
the larger one.

Fi-4.   CYLINDRICAL SOAP FILM

Two rings are mounted with tripod
type supports. One ring has a tube as
its center and the other ring has as its
center a rod which slides through the
tube. The rings, with the soap film,
may be separated by sliding the rod through
the tube. One obtains a cylindrical soap film
between the rings.

Fi-5.   MERCURY AMOEBA

A watch glass contains a small globule of
mercury in contact with a nail. A dilute
solution of sulfuric acid and potassium di-
chromate are then added. The battery action
produces a charge layer over the mercury
which changes the effective surface tension
and hence the shape of the globule. The
globule touches the nail and discharges to
give a new value of the effective surface
tension. The globule keeps pulsing much like a
live amoeba. The apparatus should be used with
vertical projection.

Fi-6.   SURFACE REACTION

A dish of water with sawdust sprinkled on the surface is arranged for vertical projection. The surface is then touched with a bar of soap and destroys surface tension in this region. The film then draws the sawdust quickly to the edge of the container.

Fi-7.   FORCE OF FILM

A "U" shaped wire has a movable wire across the open end of the "U". This closed area is then covered with a soap film. The force exerted on the movable wire by the soap film decreases the area and raises the movable wire, even when the "U" is inverted.

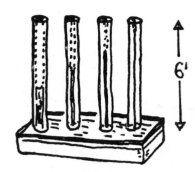

Fi-8.   CAPILLARY TUBES

Vertical glass tubes with different bores are immersed in colored water. The water rises to heights inversely proportional to the respective radii. Project.

Fi-9.   SURFACE TENSION HYPERBOLA

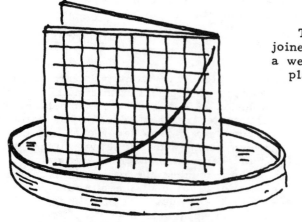

Two sheets of glass are joined at one edge to form a wedge. The wedge is then placed into a flat dish of water. The surface tension draws the water into the wedge. A piece of transparent coordinate paper, made by a copy machine, is on one of the plates so the nature of the curve can be shown.

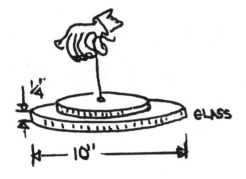

Fi-10. COHESION PLATES

Two heavy glass plates can be placed together with water between them. A string attached to the top plate allows one to lift it with the bottom plate hanging on due to surface tension forces.

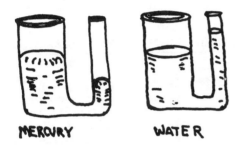

Fi-11. DEPRESSION AND RISE IN
A CAPILLARY TUBE

Two glass "U" tubes are made, each having a large bore arm connected to a small bore arm. One of the tubes is filled with water and the other is filled with mercury. The respective rising and falling of the liquids in the two tubes can easily be observed when the arrangement is projected.

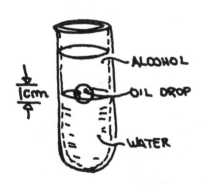

Fi-12. SPHERICAL OIL DROP

A stratified mixture of alcohol and water has regions of density equal to that of olive oil. As oil is added to the mixture, it sinks to a stable depth and collects into a large spherical drop under the action of surface tension forces.

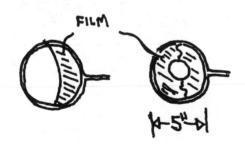

Fi-13. RING AND THREAD

A wire ring with a thread network tied across it is covered with a soap film. Various regions surrounded by thread can then be punctured, which in turn causes the thread around that open region to "expand" and produce a maximum area.

Fi-14. <u>SIZE OF DROPS</u>

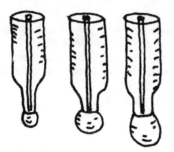

Different size flat ends are ground onto the ends of capillary tubes of identical bores. The tubes yield drops of different size when they are used as the nozzles of water droppers.

Fi-15. <u>DETERMINATION OF DROP SIZE</u>

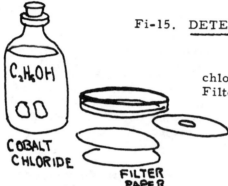

C₂H₅OH

COBALT
CHLORIDE

FILTER
PAPER

A few large crystals of cobalt chloride are dissolved in alcohol. Filter papers are then soaked in the alcohol and dried. A blue ring proportional to the size of the drop forms when a water drop strikes the treated filter paper.

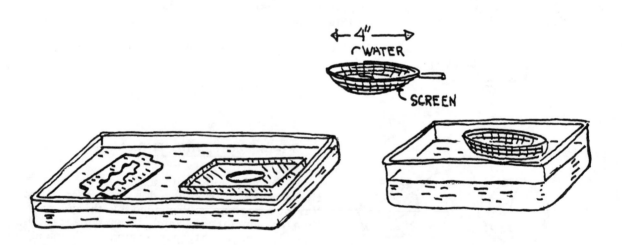

4"
WATER

SCREEN

Fi-16. <u>LEAKY BOATS (SIEVES AND RAZOR BLADES)</u>

Bowls made of screen can hold water or float on water surfaces as long as only one side is allowed to become wet. Razor blades and metal boats with holes in the bottom will float on a surface of water.

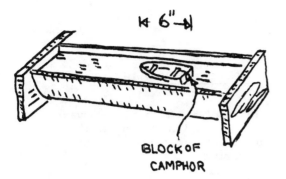

Fi-17. SURFACE TENSION BOAT

A trough is filled with water in
which a small boat can be floated. If
block camphor is attached to the back
of the boat, the surface tension of the
water is lowered in its proximity. The
larger surface tension around the front
edges of the boat pulls it forward.

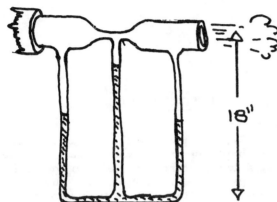

Fj-1. BERNOULLI TUBES

A glass tube with a constriction
can carry a fast blast of air. A
water manometer connected between
the constriction and the larger diameter sections shows the pressure is
lower in the constriction where the
air velocity is high.

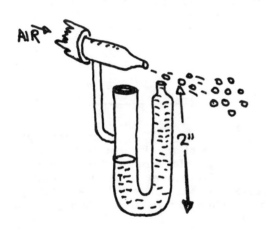

Fj-2. ATOMIZER

A "U" tube filled with colored water
has a constriction on one arm across
which a fine jet of high velocity air can
be blown. The difference in pressure
raises the liquid in one arm until it is
carried along by the jet. This can be
shown by projection.

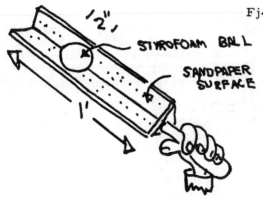

Fj-3. CURVED BALL TRAJECTORY

A ping-pong ball or styrofoam ball can be thrown with
considerable spin by a trough
shaped paddle. One can throw
curves, hops, and drops with
the greatest of ease.

F-15

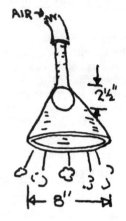

Fj-4.   FUNNEL AND BALL

A strong blast of air is sent backwards through a funnel.   A ball placed in the apex of the funnel will not be blown out and cannot be tipped out when the funnel is inverted.

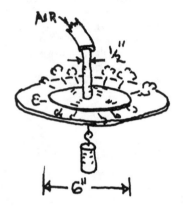

Fj-5.   LIFTING PLATE

A circular plate which has a pipe on its axis for bringing in fast moving air is fitted against a larger circular plate so that the air will escape between the two plate surfaces.   The lower plate is fitted with a hook for attaching weights.   When the apparatus is connected to a compressed air line, the lower plate will easily hold a kilogram weight.

Fj-6. STICKING PAPER FLAP

This is another application of the Bernoulli equation.   A special wooden block made similar to a whistle directs a stream of air over a plane surface.   A strip of paper is placed over the surface so that air can pass between it and the surface.   Then air is blown through, and the paper clings to the surface.

Fj-7.   PRESSURE DROP ALONG A LINE

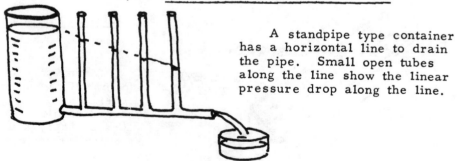

A standpipe type container has a horizontal line to drain the pipe.   Small open tubes along the line show the linear pressure drop along the line.

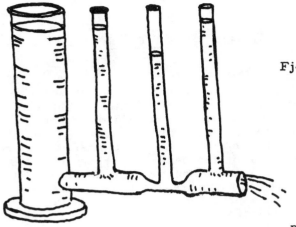

Fj-8.   CONSTRICTION IN PIPES

A large vertical cylinder is connected to several smaller vertical cylinders through a horizontal drain pipe for the system. Some of the pipes are connected at points where the cross-section of the drain pipe is large and others are connected at constrictions in the drain-pipe. The low pressures caused by the high velocities can be seen by the varied heights of the water in the vertical pipes.

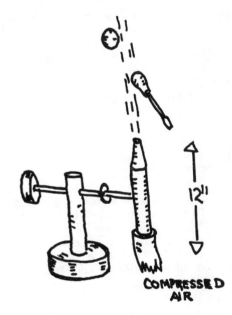

Fj-9.   FLOATING OBJECTS IN JET STREAM

A nozzle which carries high velocity air can be pointed in any direction in a vertical plane. One can then suspend objects such as balls, screwdrivers, and ice picks in the jet stream. The viscous forces of air flow balance the weight of the objects and the low pressure in the jet keeps the objects pressed against the jet.

COMPRESSED AIR

Fj-10.   LOOP THE LOOP

A cardboard cylinder is thrown with a large spin about its axis which is oriented horizontally. The large spin is given by a ribbon wrapped around the cylinder. The forward motion along with the spinning layers of air dragged by the rotation results in low pressures on top and higher pressures on the bottom. This will produce a force normal to the motion and cause the cylinder to loop.

METER STICK

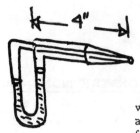

Fj-11. PITOT TUBE

A tapered cone is fastened to a piece of thin-walled 1/4" pipe which is connected to one side of a manometer. A piece of thinwalled 1/8" pipe is fitted coaxially to form a hole in the tip of the cone. The 1/8" pipe passes through the wall of the 1/4" pipe and is fitted to the other side of the manometer. Some small holes are drilled in the side of the 1/4" pipe so that it can sense the pressure in the high velocity air outside the tube. There is a stagnation point in the airflow at the tip of the cone so the small tube senses a static pressure. When the system is placed in a fast airstream, it will read a pressure difference with the manometer from which one can calculate the air velocity.

Fk-1. MARIOTTE FLASK

An open tube is inserted into a cork which serves as a stopper for a jug. Water can drain through an opening at the bottom of the jug. The velocity of efflux does not depend on the height of water in the jug, but depends only on the height between the opening and the bottom of the tube. One can move the tube up and down to obtain different flow rates. This is a convenient method of obtaining constant rates of flow of liquids.

Fk-2. VELOCITY OF EFFLUX

A tall flask has horizontal tubes which serve as openings along the side. The velocity of efflux is greatest for the opening furthest down the flask. One can show that the greatest horizontal range of the stream is realized by the tube located at a height half the distance between the top of the liquid and the surface on which the water lands.

Fk-3. TURBULENT FLOW

A long glass tube has hose connections at the two ends to serve as entrance and exit points for water. Next to the entrance port there is a bundle of 3" long small glass tubes to smooth out the flow. A glass port at the side is connected to a small tube on the axis of the larger tube. Ink is fed into the streaming water through the port. For slow flow velocities, the ink remains as a line along the axis of the tube. As the velocity of flow is increased, the line of ink will become greatly entangled, showing the onset of turbulent flow.

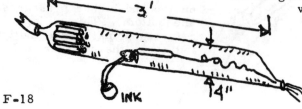

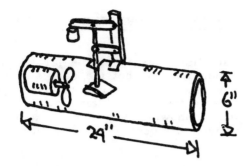

F1-1.   WIND TUNNEL

A wind tunnel is constructed from a clear plastic tube and a fan driven by an electric motor. The lift of the airplane wing section can be determined with weights.

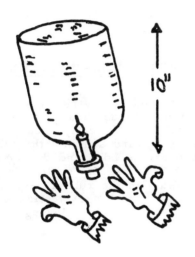

F1-2.   BOTTLE AND CANDLE

A candle is lighted and inserted into a large jug where it can burn for some time on the oxygen present. If the experiment is repeated while the jug is thrown into the air, the candle goes out due to lack of driving forces for convection currents in the freely falling system.

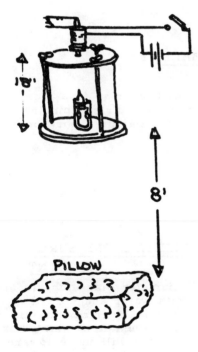

F1-3.   GRAVITATIONAL PRESSURE
IN CIRCULATION

A Plexiglas jar has a removable top so that one can insert a candle on the bottom. A lamp chimney made of a glass tube with side holes is placed around the candle. The cover is then fastened and the entire jar is suspended by an electromagnet. When the circuit is opened, the jar falls 6 to 8 feet to a cushion. During the fall the candle goes out, since there is no reaction to gravitational forces which give rise to circulation and supply oxygen to the flame.

F1-4.   CENTRAL PRESSURE GRADIENTS

This demonstration uses the same jar as that used in the previous demonstration, but the candle is placed close to the edge and the system is placed on a turntable. When rotation starts the candle flame points to the center as well as upward, showing that there is a pressure gradient which gives the central acceleration.

F1-5.   EINSTEIN'S BIRTHDAY PRESENT

A ball is attached to a string and a weak rubber band which extends through a tube. The weight of the ball is sufficiently great to keep it from being pulled upward and into the tube when the ball hangs over the edge and the system is at rest. One then tosses the system into the air, and the tension in the rubber band pulls the ball into the tube. The large plastic can is to prevent arguments about wind blowing the ball upward as the system falls.

F1-6.   FALLING BUBBLE

An air bubble in a liquid will not rise in a freely falling system. If the container is started spinning while thrown in the air, the bubble finds a position on the axis.

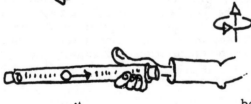

F1-7.   INERTIAL PRESSURE
GRADIENT

A 1" diameter glass tube is almost filled with water and corked at both ends. When it is inverted, the air bubble will rise to the top. When it is whirled in a horizontal circle, the air bubble will move toward the axis of rotation.

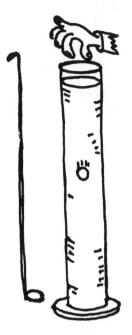

Fm-1. TERMINAL VELOCITY

If a steel ball is dropped into a graduate filled with oil, it will fall with a uniform velocity.

Fm-2. VISCOSITY OF OIL

Several sealed glass tubes are filled with oils of different viscosities. An air bubble has also been put into each tube. The tubes are mounted on a rack which can invert all the tubes at once. The air bubbles rise at different rates in the tubes and illustrate the various viscosities.

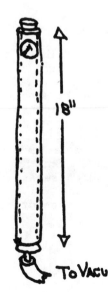

18"

To Vacuum

Fm-3. VISCOSITY OF GAS INDEPENDENT OF PRESSURE

A 3/4" diameter precision bore glass tube is fitted with a 3/4" ball bearing. The ball bearing is fitted by etching it in dilute HCl until it just fits into the tube. The speed of fall can be determined at one atmosphere pressure, and then when the tube is partially evacuated. If the fit between the ball and the tube is good, it will allow air to pass only by viscous flow, in which case the velocity is independent of pressure. The tube may also be filled with different gases to show the effects of their different viscosities.

F-21

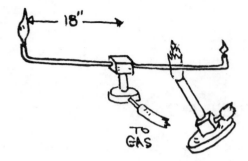

Fm-4. DEPENDENCE OF VISCOSITY
ON TEMPERATURE

Two 1/8" copper tubes about 18" long are fitted into a common gas supply. The gas flows through the tubes and is ignited on the far ends to give equal size flames. Either arm is then heated and the flame at that end becomes much smaller, showing the enhanced viscosity of the gas. This happens in spite of the fact that the hole in the tube expands.

Fn-1. COMPRESSIBILITY OF WATER

A very heavy walled closed glass container is made with a screw type plunger. The container is completely filled with water. A second container, inside, is also filled with water, and closed by a capillary tube holding a small amount of mercury. As the plunger is screwed in, the mercury plug moves down the capillary.

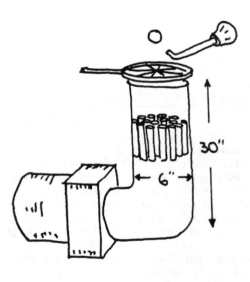

Fo-1. GROWING A
LARGE DROP

A vertical stream of air is produced with a large controlled fan. The flow pattern is made straight with a bundle of tubes. A velocity well is formed in the stream by threading strings across the diameter of a supporting ring. Large water drops are injected with a large medicine dropper. Smaller drops may be added subsequently and will rise and coalesce with the large drop.

Fp-1. VORTEX RINGS

A tobacco can with the cover removed
is fitted with a rubber diaphram. A 1"
diameter hole is drilled in the bottom of the
can. The can is then filled with smoke. When
the diaphram is tapped, smoke rings come from the can.
One can blow one ring through another with a little practice. It is also interesting to observe the interactions of the rings with surfaces. The rings spread
over the surface to from larger rings.

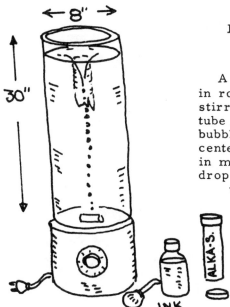

Fp-2. TORNADO VORTEX

A large cylinder of water is put
in rotational motion by a magnetic
stirrer. The water forms a vortex
tube which is made visible by air
bubbles that have centrifuged to the
center. An Alka-Seltzer tablet aids
in making the vortex visible. If a
drop of ink is added at the top of the
vortex, a mysterious sheath forms
around the vortex.

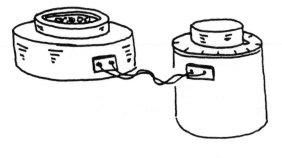

Fp-3. BENARD CELL

A heavy shallow
brass dish has a
heater fitted into the
base. The dish is
filled to a depth of
1/16 to 1/8 inches with
a mixture of molton paraffin and aluminum dust. For the
proper amount of heat and thickness of paraffin, the liquid
paraffin will break into a complicated network of convective
circulation known as Benard cells.

HEAT

Ha-1.   MERCURY THERMOMETER

Thermometers which have various ranges and are filled with various liquids are shown to the student.

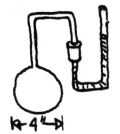

Ha-2.   GAS THERMOMETER

A bulb is connected to a mercury manometer. Heating the gas changes both the volume and the pressure.

Ha-3.   CONSTANT VOLUME THERMOMETER

The "U" of the manometer must be flexible in this case so that the manometer arm can be raised or lowered to bring the mercury to a fiducial mark at the bottom of the gas containing bulb.

Ha-4.   CONSTANT VOLUME THERMOMETER

A toilet tank float is fitted with a bourdon type pressure gauge. The absolute pressure is proportional to the absolute temperature.

Ha-5.   BIMETAL STRIP

Dissimilar metals are bonded or soldered together and fastened to a handle. When the system is heated, the metals expand differently and make the strip bend.

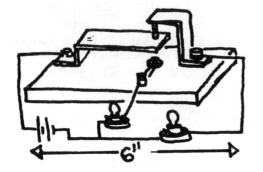

Ha-6. THERMOSTAT

A bimetal strip is made part of a single pole double throw switch. The circuit is connected so that different lights shine when the bimetal strip changes positions as a result of heating or cooling it.

Ha-7. BALL AND RING

A ball and ring are constructed so that at room temperature the ball will not pass through the ring. The ring is then heated, and the ball passes through very easily.

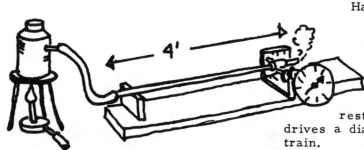

Ha-8. EXPANSION OF A TUBE

A brass tube is fitted to a steam generator. One end of the tube is fixed and the other rests on a rotatable shaft which drives a dial indicator through a gear train.

Ha-9. EXPANSION OF A FLUID BY HEATING

A flask is filled with liquid and fitted with a tube which is partially filled with the liquid. The flask is then immersed into a warm water bath. The liquid column in the tube first falls a little, and then starts to rise. Expansion of the glass flask before the liquid receives heat causes the initial fall of the liquid level.

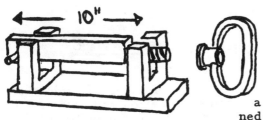

Ha-10.   FORCES CAUSED BY
          CHANGE OF LENGTH

A heavy iron bar is constructed
so that it can rest in two yokes on
a heavy base.   The iron bar is pin-
ned on one end by a 3/8 inch cast steel
pin, and the other end is threaded so that it can
be tightened between the yokes with a large nut.
The bar is heated over a bank of flames and then
tightened between the yokes.   As the iron bar contracts, it will break the pin.

Ha-11.   HOPPING DISCS

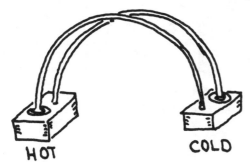

Bimetal discs are
threaded onto guide
wires.   The discs are
saucer-shaped so that
they are stable with
one curvature when hot,
and the opposite curva-
ture when cold.   The
discs release sufficient
energy in changing
curvature to hop over the
curved guide wires.   The discs will hop back and forth between
the heat source and heat sink.

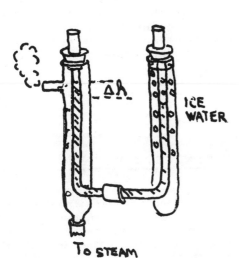

Ha-12.   EXPANSION OF LIQUIDS

A manometer is surrounded by two glass
jackets.   One glass jacket is filled with ice
water while the other is filled with flowing
steam.   The two sides of the manometer will
not be at the same height.

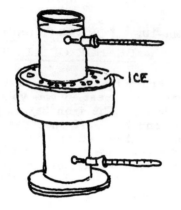

Ha-13. <u>WATER AT 4°C</u>

A cylinder of water is fitted with a thermometer at the top and bottom. An ice bath is placed around the midsection. As the water cools below 4°C, the top thermometer will go to 0°C while the bottom remains at 4°C.

Hb-1. <u>CALORIMETER</u>

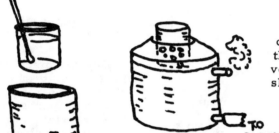

A simple calorimeter with chromed sides is used to measure the specific heat of lead. For convenience, it is best to heat the lead shot in a sort of double boiler so it does not become wet and so its initial temperature can easily be determined.

Hb-2. <u>HEAT CAPACITY</u>

Two identical beakers are placed on identical burners or hot plates. One beaker contains 1 kg of water and the second contains 0.5 kg of water and 0.5 kg of lead. Thermometers are placed in both beakers. One finds that the temperature rises more slowly in the beaker containing only water.

Hc-1. <u>CONVECTION OF GAS</u>

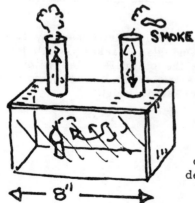

A box is made with a glass front and two glass chimneys. A candle is placed below one chimney and a smoking object is held above the other. If the system is tight, the smoke will descend through one chimney and rise in the other.

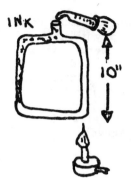

Hc-2. CONVECTION IN LIQUIDS

A closed square of glass tubing is formed with an opening at the top for adding ink. When a burner is placed under one vertical arm, the motion of the ink colored water in the tube is observed. Placing the burner under the other vertical arm will reverse the direction of flow.

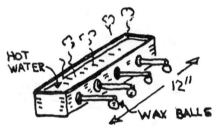

Hd-1. CONDUCTION OF HEAT

A copper container is made with stubs of different kinds of metals and insulators fastened along one side with collars. Wax balls are stuck to the outer end of the stubs and hot water is added to the tray. Heat is conducted outward along the stubs to melt the wax, thereby releasing the balls.

Hd-2. CONDUCTION OF HEAT

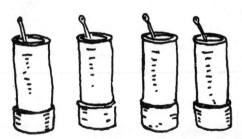

A tray similar to the one above is constructed, and used in the same way except that the stubs are painted with heat sensitive paint. As the heat is conducted outward, the color of the paint changes from yellow to orange.

Hd-3. THERMAL PROPERTIES OF DEWARS

Four dewars with identical geometries are made in different ways. One is a regular dewar with evacuated wall sections and silvered surfaces. The second is evacuated but not silvered. The third is silvered but not evacuated, and the fourth is neither silvered or evacuated. Thermometers are placed in all four dewars and equal amounts of boiling water are poured into each. The rate of cooling is then observed and one can compare losses of heat by the different heat transfer processes.

Hd-4. INSULATION WITH ASBESTOS

Two identical cans are fitted with dial thermometers. One can is wrapped with asbestos insulation. Both cans are filled with boiling water, and the relative rates of cooling are observed.

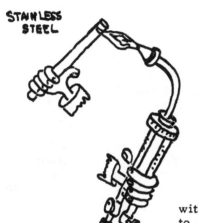

STAINLESS STEEL

Hd-5. POOR THERMAL CONDUCTIVITY OF STAINLESS STEEL

A stainless steel tube is held while it is heated with a welding torch. The tube may be heated red to white hot within an inch of the hand and still be held.

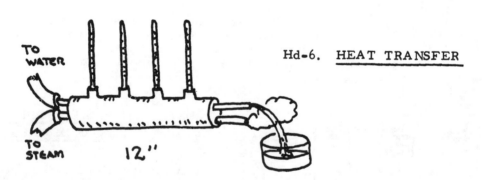

TO WATER

TO STEAM

12"

Hd-6. HEAT TRANSFER

A one inch diameter solid copper rod has two holes bored through it lengthwise. Steam is passed through one tube while cold water is passed through the other. A row of thermometers in cavities next to the water channel shows how heat is transferred at different points along the heat exchanger.

Hd-7. DAVY LAMP

Two copper screens are supported a few inches apart. A large Bunsen burner is lighted below the lower screen. Some unburned gas moves between the screens and the gas may be ignited again above the upper screen.

Hd-8. EXPANSION OF QUARTZ

A quartz tube is heated white hot with a welding torch and plunged into a beaker of water. The tube will not break. If the experiment is repeated with glass, the glass tube will shatter.

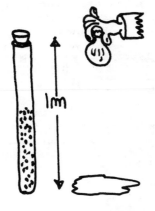

He-1. WORK INTO HEAT

(a). A long glass tube is partially filled with lead shot. The initial temperature is measured. The tube is then inverted 100 times, and the final temperature of the shot is measured. The temperature will have increased approximately $2^{o}C$.

(b). An alternative method is to have the lead shot in a bag. The bag is dropped a distance of 1 meter 100 times. Again, the temperature will rise about $2^{o}C$.

He-2. FIRE MAKER

A piece of hardwood dowel is fastened as an extension to a motor shaft. One holds a piece of soft wood against the end of the shaft with the motor running. Friction heats the wood to its kindling temperature.

He-3. MECHANICAL EQUIVALENT OF HEAT

A device similar to a Prony brake is made by wrapping copper braided wire around a copper can which holds about 200 ml of water. The can is rotated manually about a horizontal axis. One can balance the frictional torque by weights or spring balances. The torque is found from the forces and the radius of the can, and the work is found after counting the number of revolutions. A thermometer sealed into the axis of the can reads the temperature change of the known mass of water in the can. From the known heat and work, one calculates the mechanical equivalent of heat.

He-4. ELECTRICAL EQUIVALENT OF HEAT

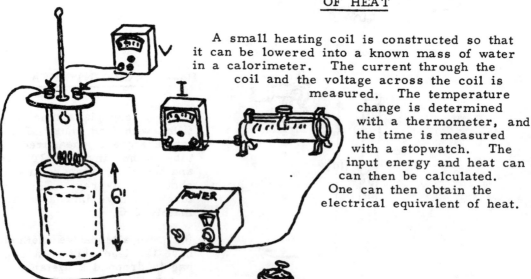

A small heating coil is constructed so that it can be lowered into a known mass of water in a calorimeter. The current through the coil and the voltage across the coil is measured. The temperature change is determined with a thermometer, and the time is measured with a stopwatch. The input energy and heat can can then be calculated. One can then obtain the electrical equivalent of the heat.

He-5. MATCH LIGHTER

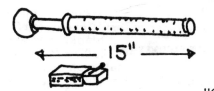

A cylinder is made with a 3/8 inch inside diameter and fitted with a slightly smaller piston rod. The piston has an "O" ring seal. A match head is placed in the piston and the system is adiabatically compressed. The match will ignite with a sufficiently hard compression.

He-6. ADIABATIC HEATING AND COOLING

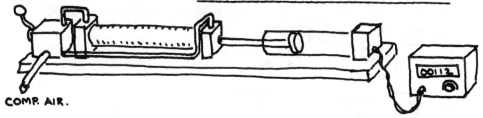

COMP. AIR.

A glass cylinder is fitted with a piston which can be driven by compressed air. A teflon block containing a thermocouple is attached to the end of the glass cylinder. The voltage from the thermocouple is registered by a sensitive digital voltmeter. The voltage will reverse sign during compression and expansion of the gas in the cylinder.

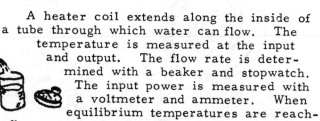

He-7. FLOW CALORIMETER

A heater coil extends along the inside of a tube through which water can flow. The temperature is measured at the input and output. The flow rate is determined with a beaker and stopwatch. The input power is measured with a voltmeter and ammeter. When equilibrium temperatures are reached, the flow rate is determined and the electric power may be compared with the power added to the water.

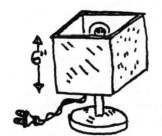

Hf-1.   RADIATION FROM DIFFERENT SURFACES

A copper cube is made with different surfaces silvered, black, and white.   A 250 watt bulb is symmetrically placed at the center. The surfaces are then viewed in turn with a thermopile connected to a good galvanometer, and the amount of radiation from the various surfaces is compared.   The device radiates mostly in the infra-red region of the spectrum so that visibly white surfaces may appear to be quite black to the thermopile.

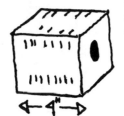

Hf-2.   HOLE IN A BLACK BOX

A black box is painted on the inside and outside with photographic black paint to make it as black as possible.   A hole is placed in the black box.   The hole is obviously much blacker than the box.

Hf-3.   RADIATION FROM A BLACKBODY

A carbon block has two holes drilled into it.   One hole is left empty so it appears very black, while the second is plugged with a white porcelain and therefore looks white in room light.   The device is then heated white hot with a large welding torch.   The black hole now appears very white, and the porcelain appears to be quite black.

Hf-4.   RADIATION FROM SHINY AND BLACK SURFACES

A heater coil is made with part of its surface shiny and part of it very black.   A piece of white paper held close to the coil becomes scorched only in the regions close to the black surface.

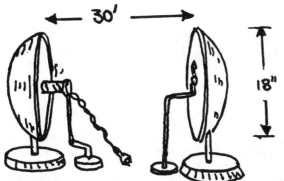

Hf-5.   TRANSMISSION OF
RADIANT HEAT

Two large parabolic mirrors
face each other about 30 feet
apart.   An electric heating coil is
placed at the focus of one mirror, while a match
is placed at the focus of the other.   When the heater is turned on, the radiant
energy is transmitted by the mirror system to the match, which will light.

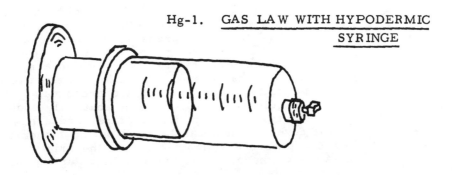

Hg-1.   GAS LAW WITH HYPODERMIC
SYRINGE

A large glass hypodermic syringe is plugged and some gas
is trapped in the cylinder.   The volume of gas is read on the
cylinder barrel.   The area of the piston is determined so the
pressure caused by an applied force may be calculated.   (The
area can be found by measuring the distance between volume
marks and dividing it into the corresponding volume.)   The
syringe can be supported vertically and weights added to give the
force.   The temperature is usually room temperature.   The device
works well for differential measurements.   If CO_2 gas is used,
the system may be adiabatically expanded or compressed to show
phase changes.

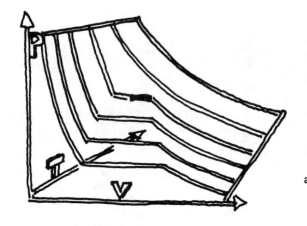

Hg-2.   MODEL OF P-V-T SURFACE

A model of the surface which
represents the equation of state
is shown by a sequence of p-V
curves with T as a parameter.
The different phases of the substance
are shown in different colors.

Hg-3.   CLEMENT'S AND DESORMES' EXPERIMENT

A 10 liter flask is filled with gas and connected
to a mercury manometer.   The flask is originally
filled to an overpressure of a few centimeters of
mercury and the gas is allowed to reach equilibrium
at room temperature.   A valve on a reasonably large
tube is then opened, and allows the pressure to adiabatically fall to atmospheric pressure.   The valve is
then quickly closed.   The adiabatically cooled gas will
warm again to room temperature, and a new overpressure
will develop which can be read on the manometer.   The
new overpressure will be less than the original overpressure.
The ratios of the overpressure can be related to the ratio of
the specific heats of the gas.

Hg-4.   ELASTIC PROPERTIES OF GASES

A piece of precision bore 1/2 inch diameter tubing
is fitted into a 2 liter flask.   A 1/2 inch ball bearing
is etched in hydrochloric acid   until it just fits into the
glass tube.   The bottom of the tube has a stopper with a
hole so that the ball will stay in the tube, but gas can freely
enter the bottom of the tube.   A small hole is drilled in
the precision tube above the cork line of the flask.   Gas
is fed into the bulb through a second smaller tube in the
stopper of the flask.   As gas is slowly fed into the system, the ball will rise past the hole in the tube where
the gas can escape faster than it is entering.   The ball
then falls and compresses the gas in the flask.   The
compression is adiabatic, so it depends on the ratio of
the specific heats at constant pressure and at constant
volume.   The system oscillates like a mass and spring
with a period that depends on the ratio of specific heats.
Helium gas gives rapid oscillations, while freon gas gives
very slow oscillations.

Hg-5. RUCHHARDT'S EXPERIMENT

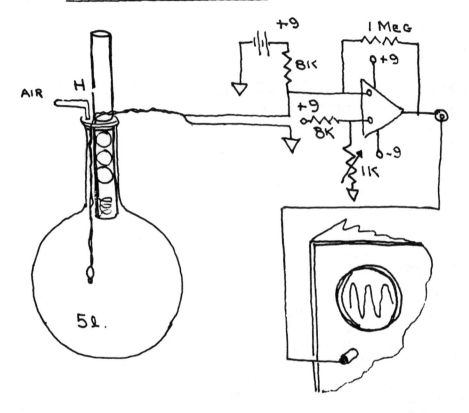

A precision bore 1" I. D. glass tube about 1 foot long is fitted into a 5 liter flask.   Three 1 inch ball bearings are etched in hydrochloric acid until they just fit into the tube.   The balls are kept from falling through the tube by a spring at the bottom. Two 0.086 inch holes "H" are bored through the tube just above the stopper.   The glass tube, an air inlet tube, and a thermistor are sealed by a stopper into the 5 liter flask.   The thermistor output is fed through an amplifier to an oscilloscope.   When air is forced into the flask, the balls rise past the hole "H" where excess air escapes and the balls fall again.   This continues in an oscillatory way.   As the balls fall they compress the air adiabatically.   The temperature change is seen on the oscilloscope.   The oscillations of the temperature are 180° out of phase with the positions of the balls.   Different gases with different values of C_p/C_v may be used to give different periods of oscillation.

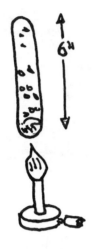

Hh-1. MODEL FOR KINETIC THEORY OF GASES

A glass tube about one inch in diameter contains a small puddle of mercury and broken glass chips. The tube is evacuated and sealed. The tube is then held in a vertical position and the region holding the mercury puddle is heated. The glass chips violently fly around the tube, illustrating a swarm of particles in kinetic motion.

Hh-2. MODEL OF KINETIC PRESSURE

Small steel shot is directed downward by a funnel onto an oblique plate which rests on one pan of a balance. The plate deflects the shot horizontally and then into a beaker. The system is in balance before releasing the shot. While the shot is falling, the system is rebalanced. The mass of shot per unit time is found by measuring the mass of shot collected in the beaker in a known time. The velocity is determined from the height of fall. One compares the rate of momentum transfer to the measured force.

Hh-3. BROWNIAN MOTION

The stage of a microscope is fitted with a small cell which can transmit light through the top and bottom. A bulb and tube are attached to the cell so that smoke from an extinguished matched can be drawn into the cell. Once the original turbulence subsides, the chaotic motion of the smoke particles can be observed.

H-16

Hh-4.   TWO DIMENSIONAL KINETIC MOTION

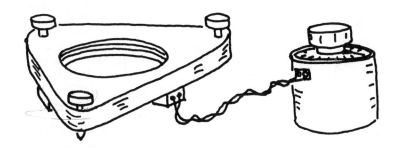

This is a device made by R. C. Plumb. It is a heavy plate which can be placed on an overhead projector, leveled, and made to vibrate with various amplitudes by means of a Variac. Glass plate inserts with different characteristics may be placed into the large plate.

One can show the equipartition of energy using different sized balls.

Using a barrier with a gap, one can show transport through the gap until the number densities of the balls are equal.

A slight well-like depression in the plate shows the potential well effect, and the nature of condensation.

Different size rings are placed (one at a time) around the depression in the plate of the above experiment. The size of the ring affects the number of balls in the well. This shows the effects of entropy.

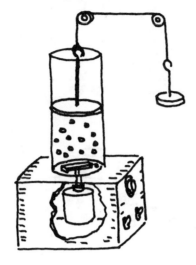

Hh-5. MECHANICAL MODEL OF
KINETIC MOTION

This model, built by Cenco, uses small lead shot to represent molecules. The "molecules" are agitated by a variable speed motor. "Heat" can be added to the system by increasing the speed of the motor. The increased motion of the shot indicates that the "temperature" of the "molecules" has been raised. The change in volume of the "gas" is given by the change in position of the piston. The counterweight on the piston gives the pressure.

Hh-6. RADIOMETER

The radiometer has four vanes, silvered on one side and blackened on the other. The vanes are mounted in a glass bulb which is evacuated to a pressure of approximately 10^{-2} mm of Hg. At this pressure, the mean free path is about the dimensions of the system so that a maximum number of molecules can carry energy between the walls of the vessel and the vanes. The momentum change is greater from the hot black surfaces where the molecules gain energy, so that the rotation is toward the silvered surfaces.

Hh-7. MEAN FREE PATH AND PRESSURE

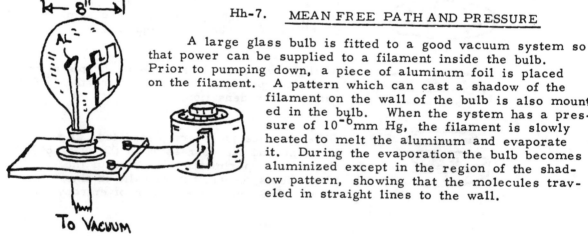

A large glass bulb is fitted to a good vacuum system so that power can be supplied to a filament inside the bulb. Prior to pumping down, a piece of aluminum foil is placed on the filament. A pattern which can cast a shadow of the filament on the wall of the bulb is also mounted in the bulb. When the system has a pressure of 10^{-6} mm Hg, the filament is slowly heated to melt the aluminum and evaporate it. During the evaporation the bulb becomes aluminized except in the region of the shadow pattern, showing that the molecules traveled in straight lines to the wall.

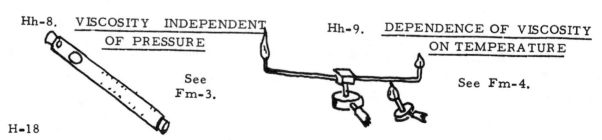

Hh-8. VISCOSITY INDEPENDENT
OF PRESSURE

See
Fm-3.

Hh-9. DEPENDENCE OF VISCOSITY
ON TEMPERATURE

See Fm-4.

H-18

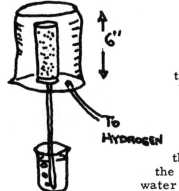

Hi-1. DIFFUSION OF HYDROGEN

An unglazed porcelain cup is fitted with a glass tube which terminates in a beaker of water. A beaker is held over the porcelain cup, and hydrogen gas is bled into the intervening region to produce a concentration gradient across the wall of the cup. The hydrogen diffuses through the cup and escapes as bubbles in the lower beaker. When the top beaker is removed allowing air to surround the cup, the hydrogen diffuses outward and sucks the water up the tube.

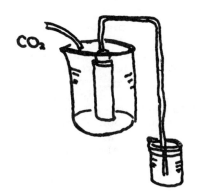

Hi-2. DIFFUSION OF CO_2

Carbon dioxide diffuses more slowly than air, so the porcelain cup described above is placed in an upright beaker. When CO_2 is flowing into the beaker, the air in the porcelain cup diffuses outward and water from the lower beaker is sucked upward in the connecting glass tube.

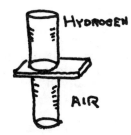

Hi-3. DIFFUSION OF GASES

Two identical glass vessels are fitted mouth-to-mouth with a cover glass plate between them. The top vessel has been previously filled with hydrogen and the bottom vessel with air. The cover glass is removed for a few minutes so that hydrogen can diffuse against buoyant forces. An explosive mixture forms in the bottom vessel.

Hi-4. DIFFUSION OF BROMINE

Bromine is a heavy brown gas. Using the same experimental arrangement as in the previous demonstration, bromine is placed in the lower container. When the cover plate is removed, the bromine diffuses upward into the air until the entire system becomes a uniform light brown color.

Hi-5. DIFFUSION IN LIQUIDS

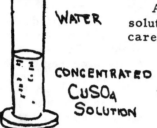

WATER

CONCENTRATED CuSO₄ SOLUTION

A cylinder is filled half full with concentrated $CuSO_4$ solution, which is more dense than water. Water is carefully poured in to fill the vessel, giving a rather sharp line between the two fluids. In about an hour the original sharp demarcation line becomes blurred over a region of 1 cm depth, and after a few weeks the entire solution is uniformly blue.

Hi-6. OSMOTIC PRESSURE

CuSO₄

WATER

A semi-permeable membrane such as a pig bladder is fastened tightly over the mouth of a thistle tube, a funnel, or a bottle with the bottom removed. Then the tube is filled with copper sulfate solution until the solution extends part way into the stem. The membrane covered mouth is lowered into pure water. After a period of minutes, the solution will rise in the stem showing that water is diffusing into the solution through the membrane. Some copper sulfate also comes out into the water, but at a slower rate.

The difference in height of the fluid levels corresponds to the osmotic pressure.

Hi-7. PREPARATION OF SEMI-PERMEABLE WALL

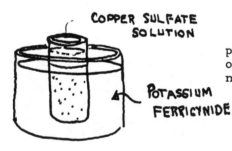

COPPER SULFATE SOLUTION

POTASSIUM FERRICYNIDE

A porous cup is filled with a solution of copper sulfate and then immersed into a solution of potassium ferricyanide. The two liquids meet in the porous walls and form a precipitate of copper ferricyanide, which is permeable to water but not to dissolved substances.

Hi-8. MEASUREMENT OF OSMOTIC PRESSURE

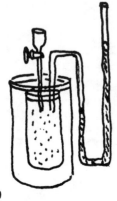

The semi-permeable porcelain cup discribed in the previous demonstration is sealed with a filling tube and a manometer. A solution is poured in until the manometer is level on both sides. The porcelain cup is then immersed into pure water. At equilibrium, the difference in heights of the liquid in the manometer corresponds to the osmotic pressure. One can show that the osmotic pressure of a solution is equal to the pressure that the dissolved substance would exert if it were present as a gas in the volume occupied by the solution. A sugar solution of known concentration works well for this.

Hj-1. VAPOR PRESSURE OF LIQUIDS

Four, meter long, glass tubes are filled
with mercury and inverted into pans of mercury so that one has four barometers. One
is used as a reference. A few drops of
water are added to the second by means of
an eyedropper which can extend into the pan
of mercury and reach the open end of the tube.
A few drops of alcohol are added to the third,
and a few drops of ether are added to the fourth
barometer. The depression of the mercury is a
measure of the vapor pressure. The fact that vapor
pressure depends on temperature may be shown by
warming the tubes.

Hj-2. ADDITION OF PARTIAL PRESSURES

A bottle is filled with air and connected to a
manometer. Inside the bottle is a thinwalled flask
of ether. The air pressure is first adjusted so there
is a pressure of one atmosphere in the bottle. The
bottle is then shaken so that the ether vial breaks.
The liquid in the manometer rises to show an increase
in pressure equal to the vapor pressure of ether.

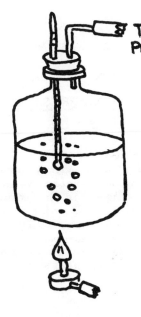

Hj-3. BOILING AT REDUCED PRESSURE

A flask is fitted with a stopper through which one
may insert a thermometer and a lead to a vacuum pump.
A flame can furnish heat to the water in the flask. As
the pressure in the flask is lowered, the temperature of
the boiling point is lowered.

H-21

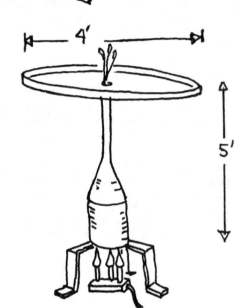

Hj-4.   BOILING BY COOLING

A strong flask with a special indented
bottom is brought to boiling for a sufficient
time to fill the entire flask with water vapor.
It is then corked and inverted.   During this
operation, the boiling will cease.   Ice is then
added to the cavity in the flask, and boiling starts
again.   The ice condenses sufficient vapor to lower
the pressure to the lower boiling temperature.

Hj-5.   GEYSER

A tall, thin, tapered tank built with a
large funnel at the top is filled with water.
The tank should be about 5 feet tall so the
pressure is considerably higher at the bottom than at the top.   Burners are placed
at the bottom of the tank to bring the water
to the boiling point.   The vapor that forms
pushes water out into the flared section
and reduces the pressure.   The lowered
pressure in turn lowers the boiling point,
causing much more water to change to
vapor.   The process is regenerative and
a geyser of water spouts from the top.
The geyser has a period of about four
minutes.

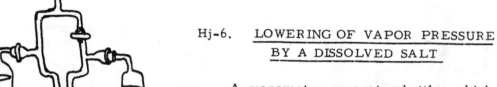

Hj-6.   LOWERING OF VAPOR PRESSURE
BY A DISSOLVED SALT

A manometer separates bottles which can
be fitted into a closed system with ground
joints.   The pressure in the system is adjusted
so the liquid in the manometer is the same
height on both sides.   A flask containing water is
attached to one side of the manometer, and a flask
containing a lithium chloride solution is attached to the
other side.   After equilibrium is reached, the manometer shows
that the flask with the dissolved salt has a lower pressure.

Hj-7. DRINKING BIRD

The drinking bird is available commercially. It is
made by blowing a glass tube somewhat in the shape of
a bird and joining it to a bulb, as shown. The bird is
filled with a liquid which has a high vapor pressure.
The bird's head is covered with fuzz to give a large evaporation
area. When the head is wet, evaporation causes cooling and condensation of the
fluid inside the bulb at the head. The center of gravity shifts to the head end
of the bird and tips it into the beaker of water where the fuzz again becomes
wet. At the same time the balance is such that the condensed fluid can flow to
the bottom bulb and shift the center of gravity back.
The process continues as long as there is water in
the beaker.

Hj-8. CRYOPHOROUS

A sealed glass tube has bulbs on both
ends and contains liquid water. The air
is pumped out so the pressure inside the tube is due only to
water vapor. The water is all placed in the upper bulb while the
lower bulb is immersed in a mixture of dry ice and alcohol. The
vapor condenses in the lower bulb and evaporates in the upper bulb.
The evaporation produces cooling, and after a short time the cooling
is sufficient to freeze the remaining water.

Hj-9. BROMINE CRYOPHOROUS

Glass tubes are evacuated
and sealed containing a few
bromine crystals. At room
temperatures, the tubes are
full of bromine gas. When one
end of the tube is immersed
into a dry ice alcohol bath, the
gas is pumped from the warm
part of the tube to form crystals
in the cold region. Some air is
left in one of the tubes, so that
one can observe the different
diffusion rates.

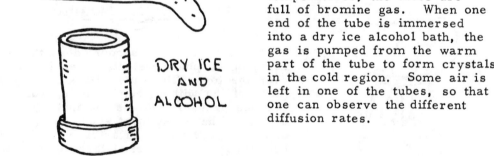

Hk-1. CHANGE OF VOLUME WITH
CHANGE OF STATE

A balloon is fitted to a test tube containing dry ice.
As the dry ice vaporizes it blows up the balloon, showing
the much greater volume of the gaseous state.

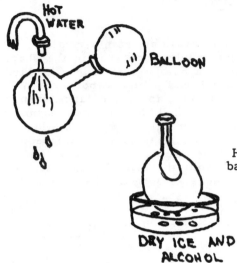

Hk-2. CHANGE OF VOLUME WITH CHANGE OF TEMPERATURE

A fairly large flask is fitted with a balloon. Hot water is then run over the flask and the balloon expands. The flask is then dipped into dry ice and alcohol and the balloon is sucked into the flask.

Hk-3. CHANGE OF VOLUME WITH CHANGE OF STATE

Equal size balloons are filled with carbon dioxide and helium. They are touched to the surface of some liquid nitrogen in turn. The balloon filled with carbon dioxide completely collapses, while the helium filled balloon just becomes somewhat smaller.

Hk-4. REGELATION

A block of ice is supported so that a wire carrying 10 pound weights on each end can pass over the top. The wire will pass through the block of ice without cutting it in two. The increased pressure lowers the melting temperature of ice. The experiment should be performed with both a copper wire and an iron wire to show that heat must be transferred through the wire from the freezing region above the wire to the melting region below.

Hk-5. ICE BOMB

A heavy cast iron bottle is filled with water and sealed with a threaded plumbing plug. The bomb is then placed into a salt water-ice bath where the water inside freezes and destroys the cast iron bomb.

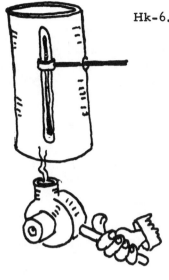

Hk-6. CRITICAL POINT OF CARBON DIOXIDE

A heavy glass tube which can stand well over 100 atmospheres internal pressure is filled with carbon dioxide so the contents are about one half liquid and one half vapor. Filling the tubes is difficult, and they must be purchased. The critical point of carbon dioxide is 73 atmospheres and 31.6°C. At room temperature one can observe the surface which separates the liquid and vapor phases. The tube is heated gently with a hair dryer to 31.6°C, and the surface separating the two phases suddenly vanishes. After the tube cools, the surface suddenly appears again. A heavy plastic shield should surround the tube at all times. THIS IS A DANGEROUS EXPERIMENT AND SHOULD BE DONE WITH GREAT CARE.

Hk-7. RUBBER AT LOW TEMPERATURE

A piece of rubber hose is cooled in a dewar of liquid nitrogen. The hose is removed and struck with a hammer. The rubber will be very brittle and break into many pieces. Similarly, a rubber ball may be solidified, and when it is thrown to the floor, it will completely shatter.

RUBBER HOSE

Hk-8. MERCURY HAMMER

A copper mold in the shape of a tackhammer is placed in an insulated box which will hold liquid nitrogen. A wooden handle is set into the form, and mercury is poured around it. Liquid nitrogen is poured into the box surrounding the form until the mercury freezes. The mercury hammer may be removed from the copper form and used to drive a nail.

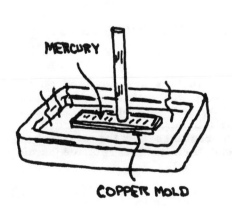

MERCURY

COPPER MOLD

Hk-9. LEAD BELL

A lead bell has no tone at room temperature. It is cooled in liquid nitrogen, and gives a very good tone.

Hk-10. VISCOUS ALCOHOL

Ethyl alcohol, which is very fluid at room temperature, becomes very viscous when it is cooled to liquid nitrogen temperature.

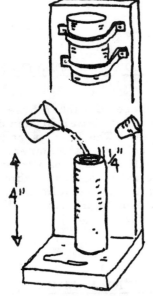
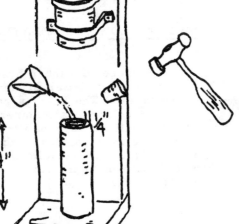

Hk-11. LIQUID NITROGEN CANNON

A cannon is made of 1/4" wall steel tubing. The cannon is partially filled with liquid nitrogen and corked with a hard wood "cork". The cork is set firmly with a hammer blow. To protect the ceiling or observers, an inverted can is placed above the cannon.

Hl-1. WET AND DRY BULB THERMOMETERS

Two identical thermometers are mounted on a panel. One bulb is kept wet with a wick immersed in water so evaporation can take place. The device is fanned, and the two thermometers are read. The difference in the readings and the dry bulb reading allow one to determine the relative humidity from the chart on the panel.

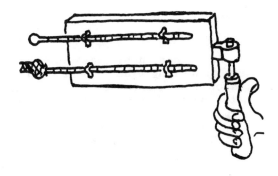

H1-2.   SLING PSYCHROMETER

Two thermometers are mounted on a panel which can be rotated. One thermometer carries a wet wick which cools it by evaporation. The relative humidity is determined from special tables after finding the difference in thermometer readings and the temperature of the dry bulb thermometer.

H1-3. DEMONSTRATION HAIR HYGROMETER

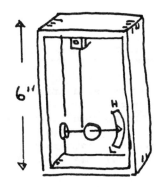

A hair is connected to a pointer system with a small counterweight. The hair expands in moist environments and contracts in dry environments. A scale is added to give relative humidity.

H1-4.   DEW POINT MEASUREMENT

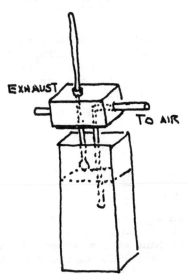

A small highly polished metal container is filled with alcohol. Air is bubbled through the alcohol to produce cooling by evaporation. The temperature is read with a thermometer placed in the thin walled cover. The shiny surface is watched for the first indication of condensation. The dew point of the air in the room is the temperature indicated on the thermometer at this time.

H1-5. DEW POINT

Two glass bulbs are connected by glass tubing, which forms a closed system containing ether. One bulb has a shiny gold band on the outside, and contains a thermometer on the inside. The ether is placed originally in this bulb, and the other bulb is immersed in a mixture of ice and water. The ether condenses in the colder bulb and lowers the vapor pressure, so evaporation is enhanced in the bulb with the gold band, producing cooling of that bulb. As cooling continues, the bulb will eventually reach the dew point and condensed water will be observed on the shiny gold surface. The internal thermometer will then give the temperature of the dew point.

H1-6. CONDENSATION NUCLEI

Steam from boiling water is passed through a damping vessel to a nozzle. Steam will come from the nozzle in an invisible column for a distance of a few centimeters and then form a cloud. If cigar smoke or discharge from a sparker is introduced, the cloud forms more readily in the invisible channel.

H1-7. CONDENSATION NUCLEI

A boiling tea kettle ejects steam into the room. If an extinguished match that is still smoking is held near the steam jet, the steam becomes much more visible.

H1-8. EXPANSION CHAMBER

A one liter flask is fitted to a rubber bulb so the gas in the bulb can be compressed and expanded at will. Water is added in sufficient amount so the squeezed bulb can force some water into the glass bulb as the air and water vapor is compressed. When the pressure on the rubber bulb is released, the gas adiabatically expands and forms a cloud of water droplets in the gaseous region. After a few expansions, the condensation nuclei are   removed as droplets and no cloud will form. If some cigar smoke or ions are admitted through the side arm, the cloud reappears on expansion showing the presence of condensation nuclei.

H1-9.   CONDENSATION AND
COALESCENCE

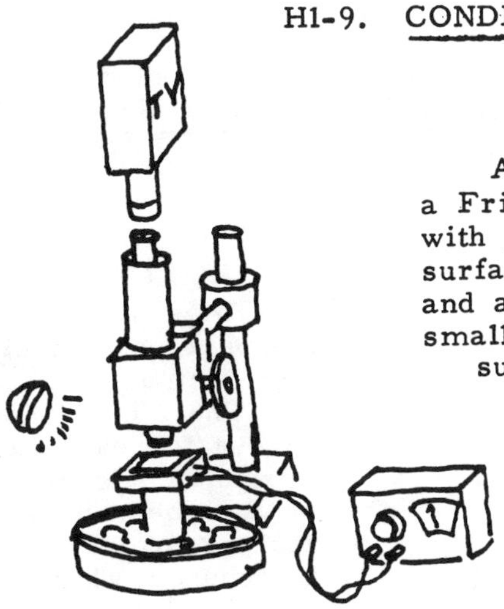

A shiny surface is placed onto
a Frigister (thermoelectric cooler)
with good heat transfer paste.   The
surface is viewed with a microscope
and a television camera.   Very
small water drops grow on the
surface.   The initial growth is
by diffusion of vapor from
room air.   Later the small
drops coalesce to form larger
drops.

H1-10.   VAPOR PRESSURE OF WATER

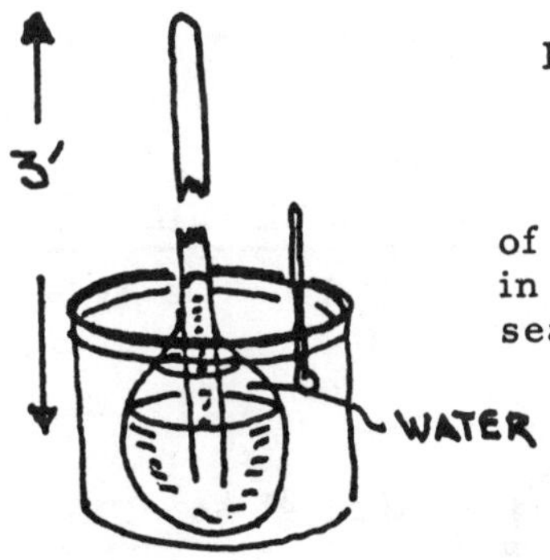

Liquid water is placed over a layer
of mercury in a bulb.   The air above and
in the water is evacuated, and the system
sealed off as a barometer.   The barometer
will read the vapor pressure of water
at any temperature.

3'

WATER

H1-11.   ICE NUCLEI

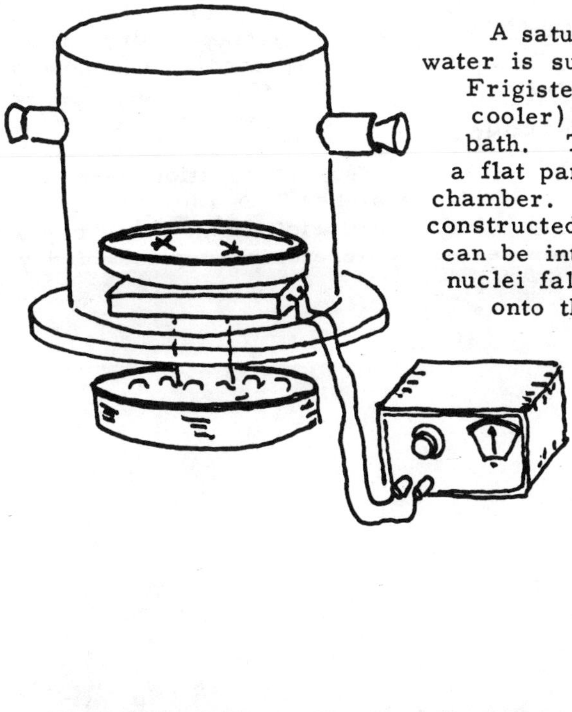

A saturated solution of sugar
water is supercooled with a
Frigister (thermoelectric
cooler) in contact with an ice
bath.   The sugar water is in
a flat pan at the bottom of the
chamber.   The chamber is
constructed so that air samples
can be introduced.   As ice
nuclei fall from the air sample
onto the sugar solution,
large ice crystals
form on the surface
of the solution.

H1-12. WILSON CLOUD CHAMBER

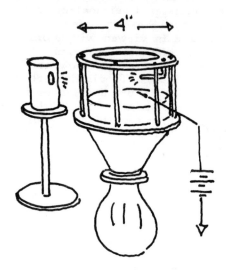

The Wilson cloud chamber is an expansion type cloud chamber that uses alcohol vapor. The alcohol contains a dark dye for ease in viewing. The expansion is obtained with a heavy rubber bulb. A permanent uranium ore radioactive source which emits alpha particles is on a wire in the chamber. A wire through the side wall of the chamber allows a clearing field to be applied.

H1-13. DIFFUSION CLOUD CHAMBER

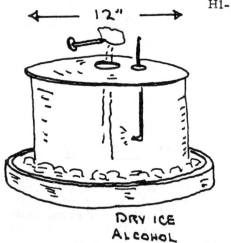

DRY ICE
ALCOHOL

This is a large glass cylinder with metal end plates. Black velvet that is soaked with alcohol covers the inside surface of each end plate. The lower end of the cloud chamber rests in a tray of dry ice and alcohol. Alcohol vapor diffuses from the warm upper plate to the cold lower plate, and gives all ranges of supersaturation vertically across the chamber. A radioactive source may be placed at the region of optimum nucleation. One can also show effects of cloud seeding by scratching a piece of dry ice over an opening in the top.

Hm-1. DUST EXPLOSION

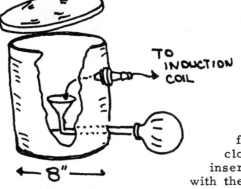

TO INDUCTION COIL

A small funnel is soldered into the bottom of the side of a large can. The funnel is connected to a squeeze bulb so that combustible dust, such as flour, may be blown into the closed can. A spark plug is inserted into the side of the can with the center lead connected to a gap at the funnel. The spark plug can be operated with a small iduction coil. The spark ignites the flour dust and starts an explosion.

Hm-2. ORDER AND DISORDER

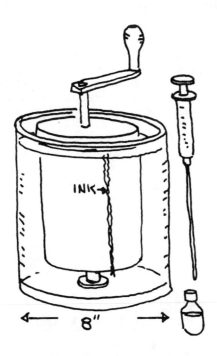

INK

A plastic cylinder, about 8 inches in diameter, contains a second cylinder with a diameter of about 7 inches. The inner cylinder has a bearing and crank so it can turn about the common axis of the cylinders. The space between the cylinders is filled with glycerine. The system should be refrigerated in an ice bath prior to use.

A column of ink is introduced into the cold glycerine with a hypodermic needle. After the ink is in place the inner cylinder is rotated, say, one turn and it appears that the ink is thoroughly mixed in the glycerine. A reverse turn is made, and the column of ink reforms. One can then repeat the experiment with two turns, three turns, etc. The column of ink always reforms when the same number of reverse turns is made. (This is the most amazing demonstration in the book.)

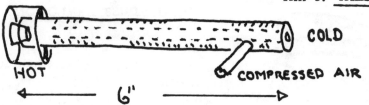

Hm-3. HILSCH TUBE

A thin walled tube, about 3/8 inches in diameter and about 6 inches long, is used. Compressed air is admitted so that it gives tangential flow about one inch from the end. A diaphragm with a small hole is placed at the cold end and a plug that leaks near the circumference is placed at the hot end. The plug is mounted so the leak is adjustable. A sort of double vortex forms in the tube so that hot air comes out at the circumference and cold air comes out the other end from the core. The tube gets very hot.

Hm-4. THERMAL PROPERTIES OF RUBBER

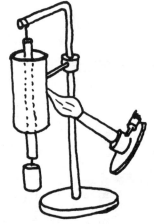

A piece of small rubber tubing is suspended inside a copper tube shield. The copper shield is heated with a Bunsen burner. The rubber contracts as it gets warm.

Hm-5. RUBBER BAND MOTOR

A circular metal rim and a good bicycle axle are connected by rubber band spokes. Rubber contracts on heating, so the center of gravity will shift if the rubber spokes on one section of the wheel are irradiated with a heat lamp. The heated, shorter spokes move out of the irradiated region and cool, as new spokes move in. The continuous process results in rotation of the wheel.

Hn-1. COMPRESSED AIR ENGINE

The compressed air engine has all of the working parts of a small steam engine, but runs on compressed air. Thermometers can be inserted in the input and exhaust to show the temperature difference.

Hn-2. LIQUID NITROGEN ENGINE

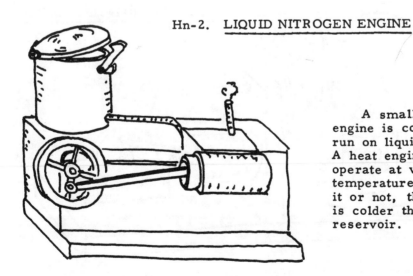

A small steam engine is converted to run on liquid nitrogen. A heat engine can operate at very cold temperatures. Believe it or not, the exhaust is colder than the reservoir.

Hn-3. STEAM ENGINE

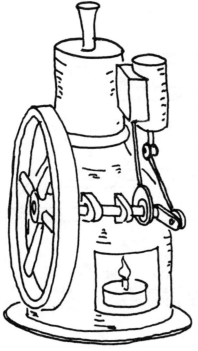

A steam engine which runs using an alcohol lamp can be shown.

Hn-4. STIRLING HOT AIR ENGINE

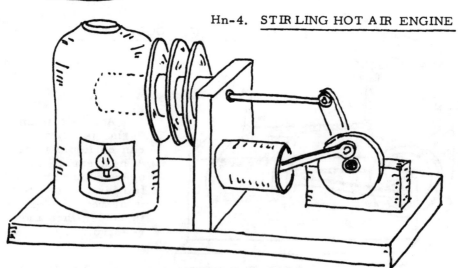

This engine operates on the Stirling heat cycle.

Hn-5. <u>HERO'S ENGINE</u>

A model of Hero's engine is made from glass. When a Bunsen burner is placed under the flask, the escaping steam makes the system rotate. The temperature of the exhaust steam is lower than the temperature of the steam in the flask.

ELECTRICITY
AND

MAGNETISM

Ea-1.   ELECTROSTATIC CHARGES

Triboelectric effects are used to define the signs of charges. A glass rod rubbed with silk has a positive charge and an ebonite rod rubbed with cat's fur is negatively charged. The components should be kept in a desiccator to keep them dry. There are many materials from which one can obtain charges due to triboelectric effects.

Ea-2.   ELECTROSCOPE

A good gold leaf electroscope is mounted in a metal case and has opposite faces which are of plane glass. One can project the actions of the electroscope by placing a point source of light behind the electroscope.

Ea-3.   ELECTROSTATIC VOLTMETER

The electrostatic voltmeter is constructed much like the electroscope except that a well balanced needle replaces the gold leaf. The needle is stable in the vertical position and electric forces are sufficient to deflect it along a calibrated scale. Electrostatic voltmeters are useful for reading voltages up to a few kilovolts.

Ea-4.   ELECTROSTATIC VOLTMETER

The voltmeter has a rotating vane with an indicator. One polarity of the potential is placed on a set of fixed vanes while the other goes to the moving vane. The moving vane is then attracted into the region between the fixed vanes to minimize the electrostatic energy of the system. Small weights can be added to the moving vane to change the sensitivity.

Ea-5. ELECTROSTATIC REPULSION

Two small pith balls approximately 3/8" in diameter are suspended by nylon thread to a common support.   The balls show strong
repulsion when they are charged with either an ebonite rod or a
glass rod.

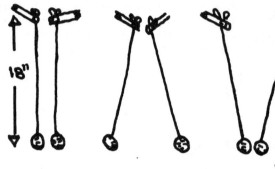

Ea-6. REPULSION AND
ATTRACTION

Two Ping-pong balls coated with
silver conducting paint are suspended
by nylon strings to independent supports.   The balls may be charged as in
the previous demonstration to show repulsion.   If they are uncharged and in
contact and then separated while in the
electric field of a charged ebonite or glass
rod, they will attract each other.

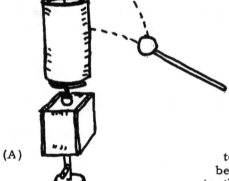

Ea-7. CHARGES ON CONDUCTORS

(A).   A copper beaker is placed on the
electroscope and charged either positively
or negatively.   A proof plane, which is a
conducting ball on an insulated handle, can be
touched to either the outside or the inside of the
beaker and then grounded before it is touched to
to the beaker again.   When the beaker is touched
on the inside, there is no removal of charge and
therefore no change in the electroscope deflection.
Charge is removed, however, if the beaker is
touched on the outside.   The charge is located on
the outside surface of a charged conductor.

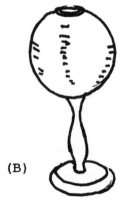

(B).   This is a more elaborate arrangement
with spherical symmetry for easier calculation.
The sphere may be connected to an electrostatic
voltmeter for quantitative measurements.

Ea-8. ELECTRIFIED STRINGS

A "mop" of insulating strings is fastened onto the end of an insulating rod. The strings repel each other when they are charged. If the strings are, say, negatively charged and a positive rod is held below, the strings will all curve inward at the bottom. If a negative rod is held below the strings, they will curve even further outward.

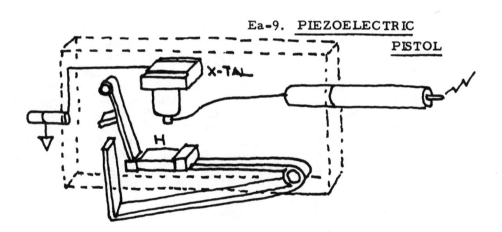

Ea-9. PIEZOELECTRIC PISTOL

This a device made by Labcon Corporation constructed so that one can squeeze it and obtain a high voltage. As the "trigger" is squeezed, elastic stress is placed into a plastic hairpin bar which carries a hammer "H". The hammer is triggered at the end of the squeeze and hits an anvil on the piezoelectric crystal. The opposite side of the crystal is connected to ground. The crystal delivers a large voltage when it is struck by the hammer.

Ea-10. SHOOTING DOWN CHARGE

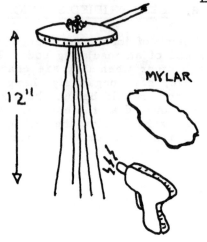

12"

MYLAR

A plastic disc with a
hole in the center supports
several strands of nylon
string. The bundle of strings
is then rubbed with a piece
of mylar. The charged nylon
strings spread out due to
electrostatic repulsion. If
one shoots at the bundle of
charged strings with the
piezzoelectric pistol described
in Ea-9, the strings collapse.

Ea-11. INDUCTION CHARGING

Special electroscopes with one
half of a metal bar on each are
initially uncharged and in electrical
contact. As a charged rod of
either sign is brought up to one
side, both electroscopes deflect.
If they are then separated in the
presence of an electric field, they
are found to be oppositely charged
with equal amounts of charge. One can
test the fact that the electroscopes are oppositely
charged by bringing the initially charged rod to each
of the separated electroscopes in turn.   The like charge
on the remote electroscope will show an increased
deflection and the unlike charge on the closer electroscope will show a decreased deflection in this
test.

Ea-12. DEFLECTION OF A WATER
STREAM

A gentle stream of water is started
from a faucet with a small opening. When
a charged rod or a recently used comb is
brought near the stream, the stream is strongly attracted to it. Water is a sufficiently good
conductor that an unlike charge is induced on the sections
of the stream in close proximity to the charged rod.

Ea-13. RAYLEIGH FOUNTAIN

A hose attached to a faucet has a nozzle
made from an eye dropper. A water stream
is then directed upward. When a charged rod
is held close to the region where the stream
breaks into drops, a charge opposite to that of
the rod is induced and held on each drop as it is
released. The drops then repel one another and give
a nice fountain effect.

Ea-14. KELVIN WATER DROPPER

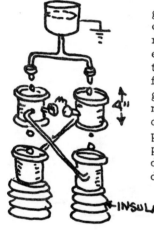

Two streams of water drops are released from a
grounded tank of water. The streams fall through
cylindrical shields open on both ends and then into
metal cups. The cups and shields are cross-connected
electrically, and the cross-connections actually serve as
the supports for the shields. The cups are insulated
from ground, preferably with teflon insulators. A spark
gap is formed between the shields. Drops leaving the
nozzles will statistically sometimes be charged. Once
one drop is charged, everything is regenerative. If a
positive drop falls to a can, the opposite shield becomes
positively charged and induces negative charges on the
drops as they leave the other nozzle. These negative
drops falling into the can make the shield for the first
stream negative, causing the induction of positive
charges on the first stream. A spark will
eventually jump the gap if the insulation is good.

Ea-15. CHARGE PROPELLED HOOP

A hoop is made of light aluminum sheet.
When a charged rod of either sign is held in front of
the hoop, the hoop is attracted toward the rod by the
gradient of the electric field.

Ea-16.   METHODS OF ELECTROSTATIC
INDUCTION

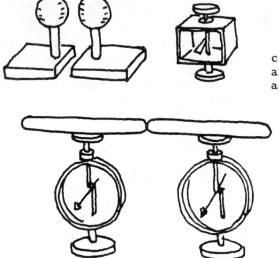

Various forms of
conductors may be sep-
arated in an electric field
and shown to be oppositely
charged after the separa-
tion.   The bodies may
then brought close to
an electroscope charged
with a known polarity.
Alternatively, one may
have the conductors
mounted on Klinger
electroscopes, which show
the charging directly.

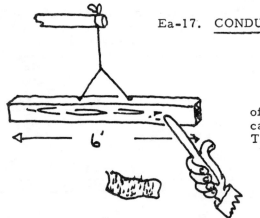

Ea-17.   CONDUCTIVITY OF A
"TWO BY FOUR"

A large 2" by 4" piece
of lumber is mounted so it
can turn about a vertical axis.
The 2" by 4" can be rotated
by a charged ebonite rod
in much the same way as
a metal rod would be
rotated.   This shows the
electrical relaxation time
of wood is less than the
time required to do the
experiment.   The 2" by 4" may
be balanced on a watch glass
instead of being suspended.

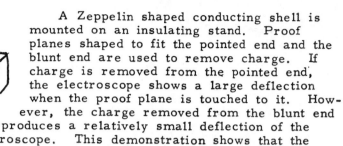

Ea-18. SURFACE CHARGE DENSITY

A Zeppelin shaped conducting shell is mounted on an insulating stand. Proof planes shaped to fit the pointed end and the blunt end are used to remove charge. If charge is removed from the pointed end, the electroscope shows a large deflection when the proof plane is touched to it. However, the charge removed from the blunt end produces a relatively small deflection of the electroscope. This demonstration shows that the charge density is greatest at pointed surfaces.

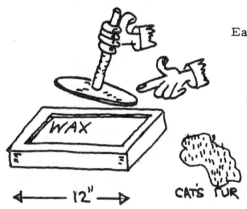

CAT'S FUR

Ea-19. ELECTROPHORUS

A tray filled with hard wax is charged negatively by rubbing the wax with cat's fur. A metal disc on an insulating handle may now be charged repeatedly by induction and used to charge many other objects with no loss of charge from the wax.

Ea-20. SHIELDED ELECTROSCOPE

A screen cage is placed over an electroscope and grounded. Any amount of electrical activity can proceed outside the cage without making the electroscope deflect.

Ea-21. BUTTERFLY NET EXPERIMENT

A long conical cotton gauze net is attached to a ring on an insulated handle. The net is electrified, and the electric charge is found to be entirely on the exterior surface. Then the net is turned inside out by using one of the two silk strings attached to the apex of the cone. One agains finds, upon testing for charge, that the charge is still entirely on the outside.

Ea-22. WIMSHURST MACHINE

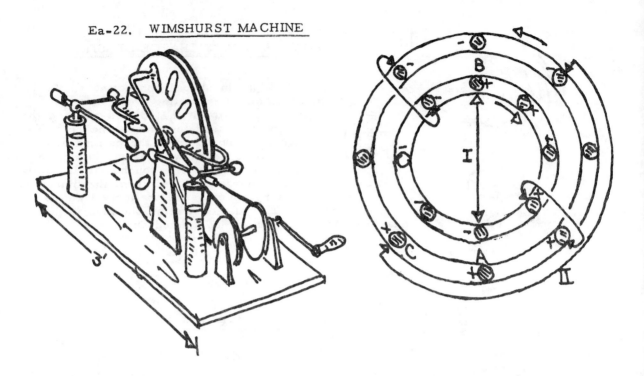

The Wimshurst machine carries out charging by induction automatically. Two large insulated discs carrying symmetrically placed aluminum foil sectors are rotated about a common axis in opposite directions. The charging process is shown schematically. Suppose the sector at A is momentarily positive. Opposite charges are then induced on opposite ends of the connecting link I and the sectors it joins on the other disc, due to the electric field of A. The positively charged sector B then moves close to the connecting link II on the first disc and induces opposite charges on the two sectors at the ends of this connecting link. The sector C is then positive and moves to play the role that sector A originally had. The positive charges are then all carried to one electrode and similarly negative charges are carried to the other electrode. Leyden jars can be connected to the two electrodes to store the charge as it is generated.

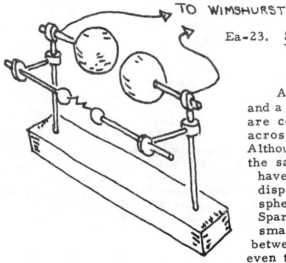

TO WIMSHURST

Ea-23. SURFACE CHARGE
DENSITY

A set of large spheres and a set of small spheres are connected in parallel across a Wimshurst machine. Although the spheres are at the same potential, they will have different electric displacements since the spheres have different radii. Sparks will jump between the small spheres rather then between the large spheres, even though the small spheres are further apart.

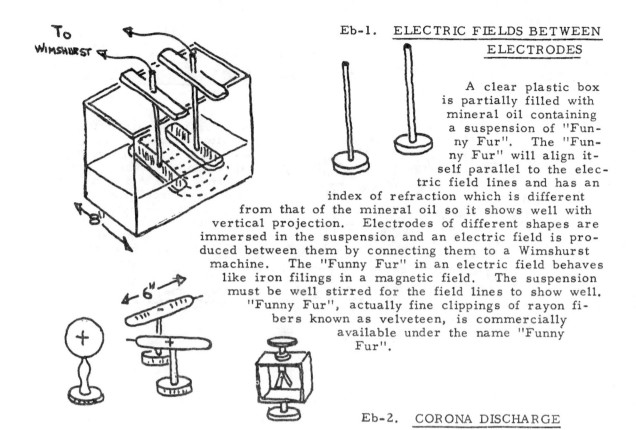

Eb-1. ELECTRIC FIELDS BETWEEN ELECTRODES

A clear plastic box is partially filled with mineral oil containing a suspension of "Funny Fur". The "Funny Fur" will align itself parallel to the electric field lines and has an index of refraction which is different from that of the mineral oil so it shows well with vertical projection. Electrodes of different shapes are immersed in the suspension and an electric field is produced between them by connecting them to a Wimshurst machine. The "Funny Fur" in an electric field behaves like iron filings in a magnetic field. The suspension must be well stirred for the field lines to show well. "Funny Fur", actually fine clippings of rayon fibers known as velveteen, is commercially available under the name "Funny Fur".

Eb-2. CORONA DISCHARGE

Aluminum cylinders with rounded and polished ends are mounted on insulating stands. A sharp needle is inserted into one end of each of the large cylinders. The aluminum cylinders are then placed near a highly charged sphere with the needle pointing toward the sphere or away from it. If the needle is pointed toward the sphere, the cylinder becomes charged with the same sign as the sphere because of the loss of charge due to corona discharge at the point. If the needle is pointed away from the sphere, the cylinder becomes charged with the opposite sign as the sphere.

Eb-3. ELECTRIC WIND

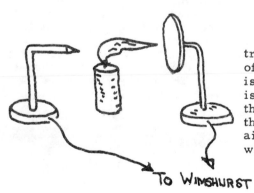

A pointed electrode and a plane electrode are connected across the terminals of a Wimshurst machine. When a candle is placed between the electrodes, the flame is blown away from the point and toward the flame. Fast moving ions produced in the corona discharge from the point drag air molecules along and create an electric wind, which blows the flame. Since the luminous portion of the flame has a net positive charge, the demonstration works best if the point is positive.

Eb-4. DISCHARGE WITH A FLAME

A pair of insulated parallel plates are charged. One plate is at high voltage, and the other is at ground. A flame connected to a high voltage source can introduce ions of desired polarity into the region between the plates.

The behavior of the different polarity ions can be studied by watching the electrostatic voltmeter.

Eb-5. ELECTROSTATIC MOTOR

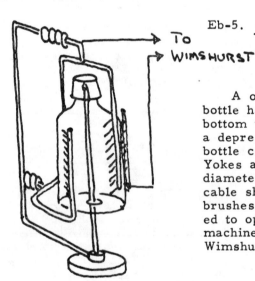

To
WIMSHURST

A one half liter polyethylene bottle has a hole drilled in the bottom to serve as a bearing and a depression in the cap so that the bottle can be mounted on a spindle. Yokes are formed across orthogonal diameters which carry cut coaxial cable shielding to form pointed wire brushes. The two yokes are connected to opposite poles of a Wimshurst machine. The bottle rotates as the Wimshurst machine is cranked.

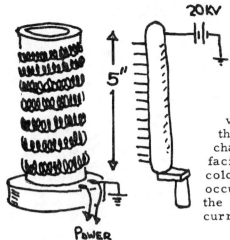

Eb-6. COOLING WITH ELECTRIC
WIND

A nichrome wire heating coil is heated until the coil is orange-red. A polished aluminum rod with several needle points is placed a few centimeters from the coil so that the needles face the coil. A variable voltage, up to 20 kilovolts, is placed between the coil and the needles to produce corona discharge from the needles. The coil elements facing the needle are cooled to a dull red or black color by the electric wind. Note that cooling occurs for either polarity of the needles, but that the cooling is most effective at a given voltage and current when the needles are positive.

Eb-7. LIGHTNING ROD

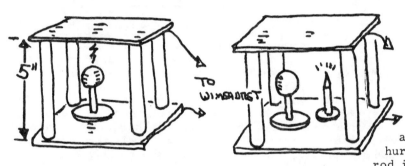

Two parallel plates are separated by insulators. A stand with a one inch metal diameter metal sphere represents a building. Sparks will jump from the upper plate to the ball when the plates are connected to the Wimshurst machine. A pointed rod is then placed beside the sphere, and one can no longer produce sparks to the sphere.

Eb-8. LEYDEN JAR

A glass jar, similar to a fruit jar, is coated on the inside and outside with aluminum foil. Electrical connection to the inside layer is made by means of a chain attached to the lid. The outside is connected by setting the jar on a metal plate. When the Leyden jar is connected across a Wimshurst machine, the sparks are no longer but they are much more intense than when the Leyden jar is not there. The jar may be charged and removed from the Wimshurst machine before discharging, and then discharged at some later time.

Eb-9. ELECTRIC CHIMES

Three metal chimes are mounted so that one
pair can be connected to a high voltage source and
the other chime to ground. Small conducting balls
are hung by insulated threads between the chimes.
When a high potential from the Wimshurst machine
is connected across the system, the balls will bounce
back and forth between the chimes as they become
charged with the same polarity charge as the chime most
recently touched. The other chime, which has the opposite
polarity charge, will then attract the ball. The apparatus may be connected to a charged isolated Leyden jar to demonstrate that energy is
stored in the Leyden jar. B. Franklin connected the double bell side to
a point on the roof of his house and used the system as a thunderstorm
warning device.

Eb-10. ELECTROSTATIC PINWHEEL

A conducting pinwheel is built with a
arm which can rotate freely and bent sharp
points on the ends. The device is placed
on an insulating block and connected to one
terminal of a Wimshurst machine. The
pinwheel will rotate away from the points for
either sign of charge, but it rotates more rapidly for
a positive polarity. The corona discharge from the point
gives the air a space charge which repels the point because the polarity is the same for the point and the air.

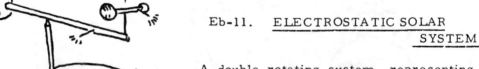

Eb-11. ELECTROSTATIC SOLAR
SYSTEM

A double rotating system, representing the
sun, earth, and moon, is mounted on axes
through the various centers of mass. Points are
then added so that corona discharge can occur
when the device is attached to a Wimshurst machine.
The action is very similar to that in the previous
demonstration.

Eb-12.   ELECTROSTATIC PRECIPITATOR

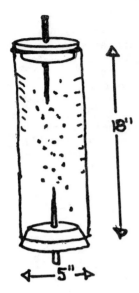

A transparent tube made of insulating material is fitted on the ends with plugs which carry pointed wires. The tube is then filled with smoke and the wires at the ends are connected to the terminals of Wimshurst machine. The smoke is quickly cleared away by the corona discharge from the pointed wires which charges the particles and sweeps them out in the strong field between the electrodes.

Eb-13.   ELECTRICAL DISCHARGE
FROM WATER DROP

A drop of water is placed on one of the electrodes of a Wimshurst machine. At a critical value of the electric field, the spherical water drop will become pointed and go into corona discharge. Since water has no free electrons, the drop does not produce corona when the charge on the drop is negative. The corona from a positively charged drop is the same as from a metal point, but if the drop is negative the electric field causes small, highly charged droplets to be ejected from the water point.

Eb-14.   EFFECT OF CHARGE ON SURFACE
TENSION

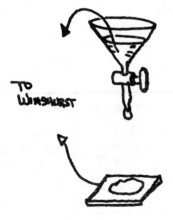

A funnel filled with water has a drip nozzle with a stopcock so that the flow of water through the nozzle can be adjusted to give any desired dripping rate. The water is then connected to a Wimshurst machine by means of a wire immersed in the water and the rate of dripping for the same stopcock setting is much greater than before. The effective surface tension is decreased by the electric charge, making it more difficult for the drop to cling to the nozzle.

Eb-15. MODEL OF MILLIKAN OIL DROP EXPERIMENT

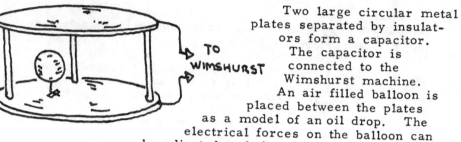

Two large circular metal plates separated by insulators form a capacitor. The capacitor is connected to the Wimshurst machine. An air filled balloon is placed between the plates as a model of an oil drop. The electrical forces on the balloon can be adjusted to balance the gravitational forces on the balloon.

Ec-1.   ELECTROSTATIC GENERATOR

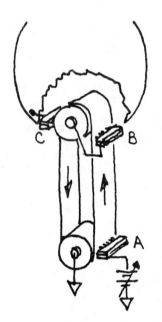

Spray bars are made by clamping shielding taken from coaxial cable between metal bars and then making a lengthwise cut with a scissors. The pointed ends of the shielding are combed out and trimmed to a uniform length.

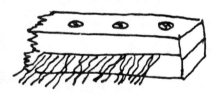

It is best to use three spray bars on the machine and to have the top pulley insulated from the ball. The bottom pulley is grounded. Charge of either polarity is sprayed onto the cotton canvas moving belt. A voltage of about 15 kv is applied to spray bar "A". The spray bar "B" is placed across the belt just below the top pulley and is connected to the top pulley. The top pulley is at the highest potential in the machine. Spray bar "C" looks directly at the top pulley through the downward moving belt and is electrically connected to the ball. At balance, charge is carried both up and down by the belt. The exterior of the ball must be highly polished. All the edges of the ball must be rounded and looking inward.

Ec-2.   LINES OF FORCE

Confetti is placed on the ball of the electrostatic generator. When the generator is started, the confetti collects charge of the same sign as the ball and is repelled
from the ball. The confetti starts its trajectory along lines
of force from the ball.

Ec-3.   LINES OF FORCE

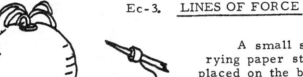

A small stand car-
rying paper strips is
placed on the ball of the
electrostatic generator.
The paper becomes charged
and stands erect, the strips
repelling each other and being
repelled by the ball.   If a grounded point is brought in the proximity of
the ball, the corona discharge from the point gives
space charge of opposite polarity to the charge on the
ball.   The space charge neutralizes the charge on the
paper strips and makes them collapse.

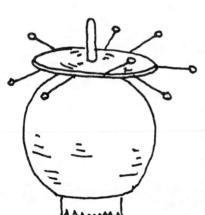

Ec-4.   PITHBALL PLATE
AND FLYING BALLS

A plate with many pith balls
on strings rests on the top ball of
an electrostatic generator.   As the
balls become charged, they extend
outward under the electric field
forces.   A cup filled with styrofoam
balls can be placed on the upper
ball of the electrostatic generator
as another experiment.   The
styrofoam balls will become charged
and will be thrown out of the cup
along electric field lines.

Ec-5. FORCES BETWEEN ELECTRODES

A six inch diameter ball is mounted on a flexible rod and grounded. As the ball is put near the sphere of an electrostatic generator, charge of the opposite polarity is induced on the grounded ball. The attractive force due to the induced charge will make the support rod bend toward the generator. When a spark occurs, neutralizing the charge on the grounded ball, the support rod straightens.

Ec-6. ELECTROSTATIC PING-PONG

COTTON BALL

A fluffy cotton ball is released near the electrostatic generator while the generator is operating. When the cotton touches the ball, it picks up a charge of the same polarity and is repelled away from the machine. The instructor has a lighted cigar which he places in the contemplated path of the ball. Ions of opposite polarity to the generator leave the ball and travel along lines of force to the cotton ball, which then becomes charged with opposite polarity to that of the machine. The ball is attracted back to the generator and the process is repeated.

Ec-7. ELECTRIC FIELD INDICATOR

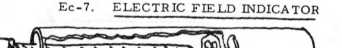

A 200 to 500 megohm resistor has one end connected to a sharp needle and the other end connected to a neon bulb. A capacitor of approximately 0.002 microfarads is connected across the bulb. The device is waxed into a Textolite tube for insulation and so it can be handled. The rate of blinking of the bulb is proportional to the electric field strength. The bulb is observed through a window in the tube.

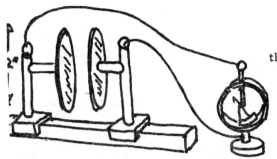

Ed-1. FIELD AND VOLTAGE

A parallel plate capacitor is built so the distance between the plates may be varied. Once the capacitor is charged, the field is essentially constant between the plates. One can then show that the voltage is proportional to the distance between the plates.

Ed-2. DIELECTRICS

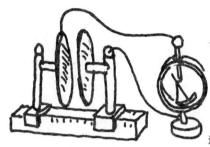

The apparatus is the same as for the previous demonstration. After charging the plates are placed rather close together, allowing just enough room to insert slabs of dielectrics. When the dielectric slabs are inserted between the charged plates, the electric displacement remains constant and the electric field decreases. Since the distance between the plates is constant, the change in the electric field is proportional to the change in voltage.

Ed-3. DISSECTIBLE CONDENSER

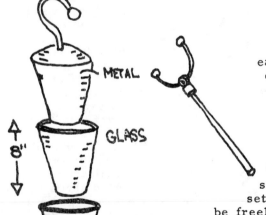

METAL

GLASS

8"

METAL

A capacitor is made which can be easily taken apart. When assembled, the capacitor is charged with a Wimshurst machine. The connections to the Wimshurst machine are removed with insulating rods, to avoid discharging the capacitor. Then the inside can is lifted out using the insulating rod. Once it is out, the inside can may be handled freely. The extended lip of the glass insulating section is then lifted out with the hand and set on the table. The bottom can may then be freely handled also. The system is then reassembled in the reverse order, remembering that the inside can must be lowered into place with the insulated rod. A large spark between the outside and inside cans is drawn with the discharge rod after the reassembly is completed. Where was the charge when the system was disassembled? The charge was bound in the glass. If the glass is replaced by quartz, the experiment will not work.

Ed-4. BREATH FIGURES

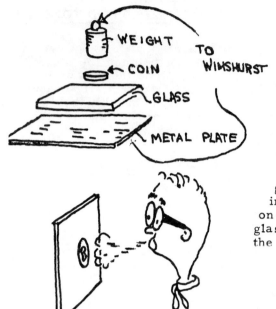

A metal plate, a clean dry glass plate, a coin, and a weight to hold the coin are stacked. The weight and the bottom plate are attached to a running Wimshurst machine for a few minutes. The system is disassembled. One then blows on the glass plate and condensation takes place in such a way that a perfect image of the coin is formed. The glass may be stored for weeks, and the image will still be there when one blows on the plate. The polarization of the glass persists and affects the places that the polar water molecules can land.

Ed-5. ELECTRIC FIELD MILL

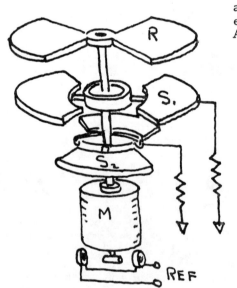

The electric field mill is a device that measures electric field strength directly. A well grounded rotor "R" is driven by a motor "M" over two sets of insulated stator plates, "S_1" and "S_2". Each stator is connected to ground through a one megohm resistor. As the rotor covers and uncovers the stators, the charge which is induced on the stators by the electric field flows on and off from ground through the resistors and generates a signal which must be amplified. The position of the rotor is indicated by the signal obtained by rotating a bar magnet past some coils. The magnet signal, known as a reference signal, can be used as a switching signal to determine the polarity of the electric field. The magnitude of the electric field is found from the currents that flow through the one megohm resistors.

Ed-6. DISCHARGE OF A CAPACITOR

An electrolytic capacitor is charged with a battery. It is then discharged through the resistance of a multirange meter. The time constant (product of the meter resistance and the capacitance of the selected capacitor) is adjusted so that the voltage on the meter can be read during the charge decay.

Ed-7. CHARGE ON A CAPACITOR

LIGHT

$\equiv$ (CM)

BALLISTIC
GALVANOMETER

A capacitor is charged with a battery and discharged through a ballistic galvanometer. The deflection is projected by means of a light beam reflected from a mirror attached to the galvanometer coil. The deflection by be obtained with various voltages and capacitors to argue that $Q = CV$.

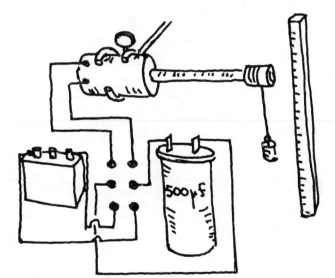

Ed-8. ENERGY STORED IN A CAPACITOR

A 500 μf electrolytic capacitor is charged to a known voltage. The capacitor is then discharged through a small motor which can raise a weight. The energy stored in the capacitor is compared with the work done in raising the weight.

Ee-1.   COPPER FLASHING OF IRON

A polished iron strip is dipped into a solution of copper sulfate. When the strip is withdrawn after a few minutes, one finds that a surface of copper has been deposited over the iron. This demonstration shows how ions can be exchanged at an electrode.

Ee-2.   DEPENDENCE OF EMF ON ELECTRODE MATERIAL

Two stands hold strips of different metals which can extend into a beaker of dilute sulfuric acid. Different electromotive forces are measured by the voltmeter as various pairs of electrodes are dipped into the acid solution.

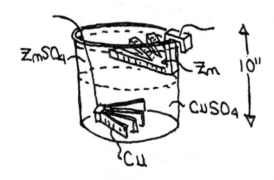

Ee-3.   CROWSFOOT OR GRAVITY CELL

A piece of zinc metal and a piece of copper metal are shaped to have rather large surface areas. A gravity separated solution of copper sulfate on the bottom is in contact with a zinc sulfate solution on the top. Each metal is then in a solution of one of its own salts. The battery can be used as a source of energy for other experiments.

Ee-4.   STORAGE BATTERY

Two lead plates are suspended in a solution of sulfuric acid. The battery is charged rapidly by connecting it to a D.C. generator through a dropping resistor. After a couple minutes of charging, the battery is discharged through a large doorbell. The battery may be charged for different lengths of time, and the bell will ring correspondingly long. It is instructive to place a voltmeter across the battery during charging and discharging.

E-22

Ef-1. CONDUCTIVITY OF SOLUTIONS

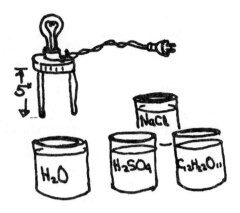

A light bulb is in series with two electrodes. The electrodes may be dipped into
distilled water or a sugar solution and the
bulb will not light. If the electrodes are
dipped into a dilute acid, base, or salt, the
bulb glows brightly.

Ef-2. ELECTROLYSIS OF WATER

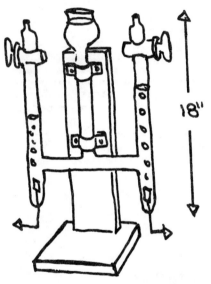

Water made slightly acidic with sulfuric
acid is placed in an "H" tube with two platinum
electrodes. When a voltage is placed across the
electrodes, hydrogen and oxygen gas are collected. The evolved gas may be collected with an
inverted test tube and exploded.

Ef-3. SPEED OF IONS

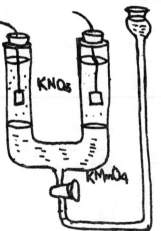

The thistle tube is filled with an aqueous solution of potassium permanganate (1/2 g per liter)
and 5 g of urea per 100 cm^3 solution (to increase
the density). The stopcock is opened until the
permanganate solution reaches the bottom of the
U-tube. The U-tube is then filled with a solution
of 0.3 g of potassium nitrate per liter of water.
After filling, the permanganate level is raised to
give a sharp edge. On passing about 0.4 amps
between the platinum electrodes in the potassium
nitrate solution, the level of the permanganate
solution rises in the anode limb and falls in the
cathode limb. The violet color migrates in the
direction of the negative current.

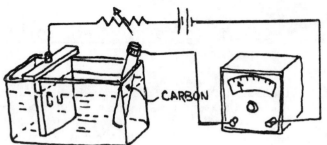

Ef-4.   ELECTROPLATING
COPPER

A copper electrode and a carbon electrode are placed into a tank of copper sulfate solution. The copper electrode is then connected to the positive terminal of a battery and the carbon electrode terminal to the negative terminal through a dropping resistor as shown. An ammeter is placed in series so that the amount of copper deposited by different currents in different times may be visually compared. A set of electrodes should be available for visual inspection of the relation between the amount of copper deposited and the amount of current passed.

Ef-5.   SILVER
COULOMBMETER

A silver electrode is immersed in a solution of silver nitrate. The cathode is a platinum cup which may be weighed before and after the experiment to determine the mass of silver transferred. If the time is measured, the value of the ampere may be established.

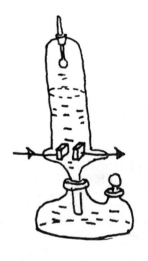

Ef-6.   GAS COULOMBMETER

Current is passed between two platinum electrodes immersed in a dilute sulfuric acid solution. Hydrogen and oxygen are collected as a mixture in a region where the volume of gas can be measured. A thermometer is placed in the region of the collected gas to measure the gas temperature. The pressure can be determined by correcting the barometer reading for the height of the water column. The mass of the gas mixture can then be calculated and related to the charge passed.

E-24

Eg-1. MODEL OF RESISTANCE

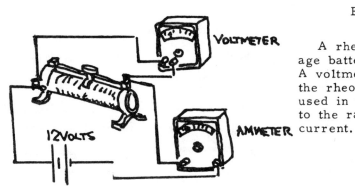

A board is pounded randomly full of nails,
spaced so that a ball bearing can roll between
them.   The balls are rolled through the maze
of nails.   Boards with different nail spacings
may be used to show varying mean free paths.
Different numbers of balls may be used to
show different numbers of charge carriers.
The board may be inclined at different angles to
illustrate the effects of applied E.M.F..

Eg-2. OHM'S LAW

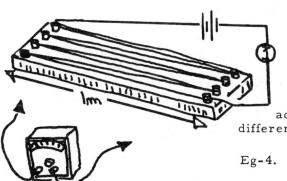

A rheostat, ammeter, and storage battery are connected in series.
A voltmeter is connected across
the rheostat.   The length of wire
used in the rheostat is proportional
to the ratio of the voltage to the
current.

Eg-3. CHARACTERISTIC RESISTANCES

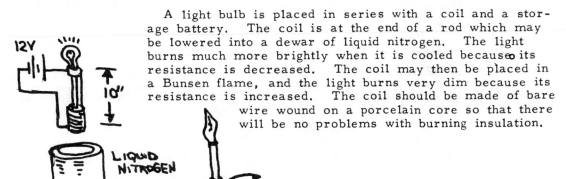

A board is constructed which
can carry several one meter lengths
of wire connected in series.   The
wires have different known cross-sectional areas and are of different materials.   The arrangement provides
that they all carry the same current.
A good voltmeter is then connected
across various sections to show the
different values of resistance.

Eg-4. TEMPERATURE DEPENDENCE
OF RESISTANCE

A light bulb is placed in series with a coil and a storage battery.   The coil is at the end of a rod which may
be lowered into a dewar of liquid nitrogen.   The light
burns much more brightly when it is cooled because its
resistance is decreased.   The coil may then be placed in
a Bunsen flame, and the light burns very dim because its
resistance is increased.   The coil should be made of bare
wire wound on a porcelain core so that there
will be no problems with burning insulation.

Eg-5. POSITIVE AND NEGATIVE RESISTANCE COEFFICIENTS

A lightbulb and ammeter are connected in series to a variable voltage. A voltmeter is placed across the lightbulb. One measures the resistance as a function of the current. A tungsten bulb will have a positive coefficient of resistance, while a carbon filament will have a negative temperature coefficient of resistance.

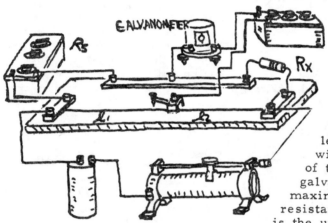

Eg-6. WHEATSTONE BRIDGE

A Wheatstone bridge, which is used to measure resistance, is made with uniform iron wire one meter long. Two of the resistances are the lengths l_1 and l_2 of the iron wire which are on the two sides of the movable tap key when the galvanometer draws no current at maximum sensitivity. The known resistance R_S is a dial box, and R_x is the unknown resistance.

Eg-7. POTENTIOMETER

A potentiometer is made with a piece of uniform iron wire one meter long. Lengths of wire at balance with the standard cell and then with the unknown cell are measured and are proportional to the electromotive forces of the cells.

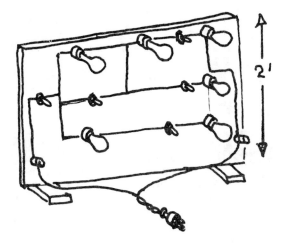

Eh-1. SERIES AND PARALLEL
LIGHT BULBS

A board is made which allows one
to switch light bulbs in and out of the
circuit. Similar or different size light
bulbs may be switched in and out to
give several combinations. The brightness of the bulbs indicates how the currents are flowing for different series
and parallel combinations of resistance.

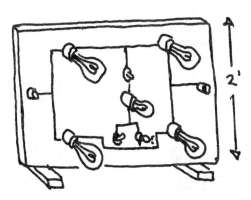

Eh-2. LIGHT BULB
WHEATSTONE BRIDGE

Four light bulbs are built into a Wheatstone bridge. The balance detector is also
a light bulb. Pairs of different sized bulbs
may be inserted in different places to
show different balance conditions. The
final balance can be shown with a low
voltage flashlight bulb.

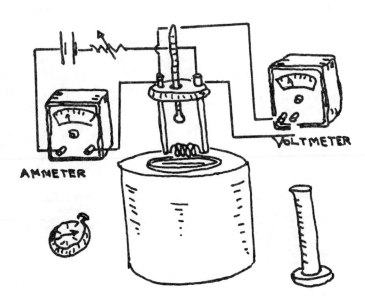

Eh-3. HEAT AND
ELECTRICAL ENERGY

A heating coil which can
be immersed into a known
mass of water is connected in
series with an ammeter, control rheostat, and storage
battery. A voltmeter measures
the voltage across the coil.
A thermometer is used to determine the temperature rise
of the water. The electrical
energy can then be compared
with the thermal energy.

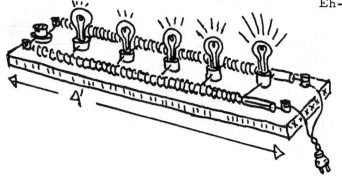

Eh-4. TRANSMISSION OF POWER

Five 200 watt bulbs are connected in parallel along two rods wound with iron wire to give a low resistance. The bulbs are successively dimmer as one proceeds down the line. Provision is made for connecting an appliance, such as a toaster, at the far end of the line.

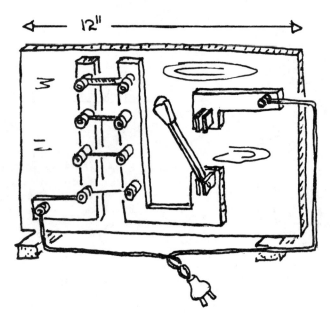

Eh-5. FUSES

Heavy copper conductors are arranged on a board so that different sizes of fuse wire may be connected across them. One observes that the large fuse wire burns out first.

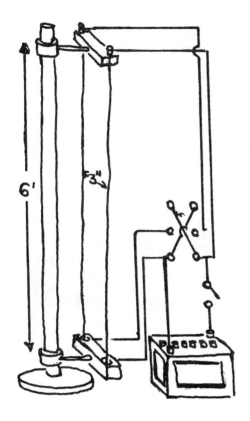

Ei-1.   FORCE BETWEEN PARALLEL
WIRES

Two wires are suspended vertically
about 3 inches apart and in such a
fashion that they are slightly loose.
The wires are connected to a storage
battery or high current DC supply either
with current traveling in the same direction in the two wires or with the currents
in opposite directions in the two wires.
For the case when the currents are
parallel, the wires will attract each other,
and they will repel each other when the
currents are antiparallel.

Ei-2.   DANCING SPIRAL

A limp copper spiral is suspended vertically with the lower end dipping into a cup
of mercury. Current is then passed through
the spiral, and will be carried in parallel
elements which are quite close to one another.
As a result, the spring will contract and
pull its lower end out of the mercury.
Since the electrical contact is broken, there
is no current and the spring again extends to
make contact.   The process is repeated,
making the spiral "dance".

Ei-3.   INTERACTING
SOLENOIDS

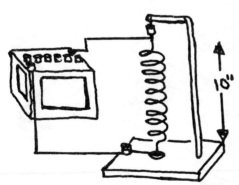

Two solenoids are wound
from heavy copper wire and
mounted with the ends in mer-
cury-filled cups located on a
vertical axis.   The coils have
horizontal axes.   Current from
a storage battery is passed in
either direction through the coils.   The coils
form poles which interact similar to bar magnets.

Ei-4.   FORCE BETWEEN RADIAL WIRES

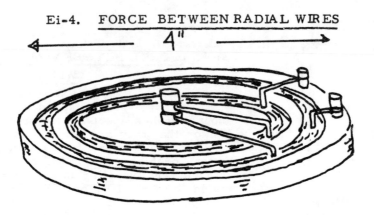

A plastic sheet is milled with two connecting circular
channels for mercury. Movable arms, much like the hands of a
watch, extend from a rotating joint at the axis, where they are
in good electrical contact. A current is made to flow from one
channel to the other via the arms. The arms will spring apart
when current flows.

Ei-5.   CURRENT BALANCE

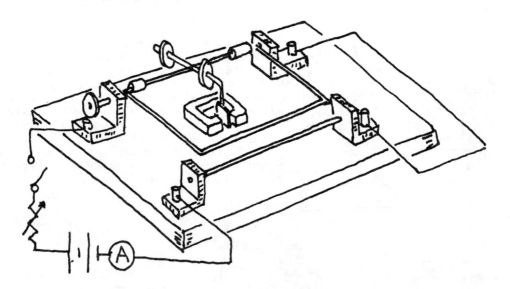

Apparatus built by Welch allows one to measure the force
between known lengths of wire separated a known distance. The
measured current runs in opposite directions in the wires. A
damping disc and adjustable screws on an insulated axis make it
possible for the system to be brought into balance.

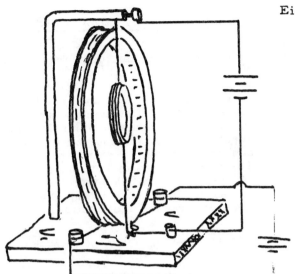

Ei-6.   INTERACTION OF FLAT COILS

A large flat coil and a small flat coil are arranged so that they can have a common horizontal axis.   The small coil is free to turn about a vertical axis.   Independent currents may be sent through the two coils. The small coil will always orient it- self so that the current circulates in the same direction in the two coils.

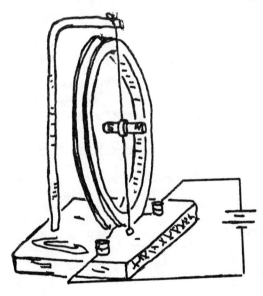

Ei-7.   INTERACTION OF FLAT COIL AND BAR MAGNET

The arrangement is similar to that of the previous demonstration except that a bar magnet replaces the small coil.   When the current is reversed in the large coil, the magnet flips around.

Ei-8.   MAGNETIC FIELD AROUND A LONG WIRE

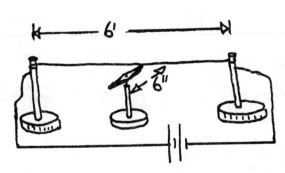

A current carrying wire is stretched across the lecture bench.   A compass needle placed near the wire turns so it is at right angles to the wire.   If the direction of the current is reversed, the direction of the needle reverses also. If the compass needle is moved from below the wire to above the wire, its direction will reverse.   The right hand rule can be established from the results of this demonstration.

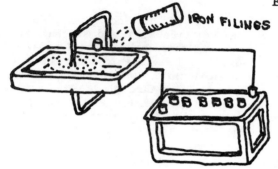

Ei-9. MAGNETIC FIELD AROUND A WIRE

A heavy conducting wire is mounted so that a vertical section of the wire passes through a transparent sheet of glass. With current from a storage battery flowing through the wire, iron filings are sprinkled on the sheet and align themselves to form concentric circles around the wire. The wire gets quite hot, so one should be prepared to work quite fast. It is usually necessary to tap the glass plate and reduce the friction.

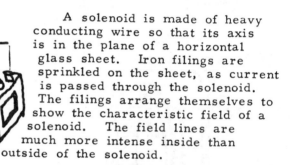

Ei-10. FIELD OF A SOLENOID

A solenoid is made of heavy conducting wire so that its axis is in the plane of a horizontal glass sheet. Iron filings are sprinkled on the sheet, as current is passed through the solenoid. The filings arrange themselves to show the characteristic field of a solenoid. The field lines are much more intense inside than outside of the solenoid.

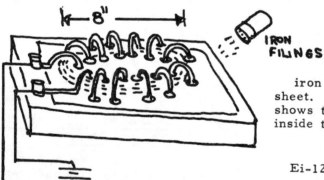

Ei-11. FIELD OF A TOROID

A toroidal winding of heavy wire is mode through a horizontal glass sheet. When current is flowing through the toroid, iron filings are sprinkled onto the sheet. The arrangement of the filings shows that a magnetic field exists only inside the toroid.

Ei-12. MAGNETIC FORCE ON A WIRE

A flexible wire is placed between the poles of a large alnico magnet. When current is sent through the wire in one direction, the wire vigorously jumps out the opening between the poles. When the current is reversed, the wire clings strongly to the "U" end of the magnet. The left hand motor rule can be established with this experiment.

Ei-13. FORCE ON A CONDUCTING FLUID

A flat dish is lined on the inside with a copper strip which serves as an electrode. A second electrode is placed on the axis. A conducting salt solution is then placed in the region between the electrodes, and the device is placed on one pole of a strong alnico bar magnet. When current is passed through the system, the fluid will rotate about the axial electrode. The direction of rotation reverses if the current is reversed. The direction of rotation also reverses when the magnet is inverted.

Ei-14. ELECTROMAGNETIC PUMP

A glass tube is blown to form a closed loop except for a nozzle and a sink. A pair of heavy electrodes is mounted in two side arms of the tube so that current flowing between them will be in a direction transverse to any motion of fluid in the tube. A large alnico magnet is used to provide a magnetic field at right angles to both the current and fluid flow directions. The tube is then filled with mercury. As current from a storage battery passes between the electrodes, the mercury is driven around the tube.

Ei-15. BARLOW WHEEL

A copper disc is mounted so that it can turn freely about a horizontal axis. The bearing surface at the axle must be able to carry a large current. The bottom of the wheel dips into a trough of mercury connected to a second electrode. When a storage battery is put into the circuit, current flows radially from the axle to the mercury. A magnetic field at right angles to the motion of the wheel and to the current is created by a large magnet. The interaction between the field and the current will make the wheel rotate. Reversing the current or the magnetic field will reverse the direction of rotation.

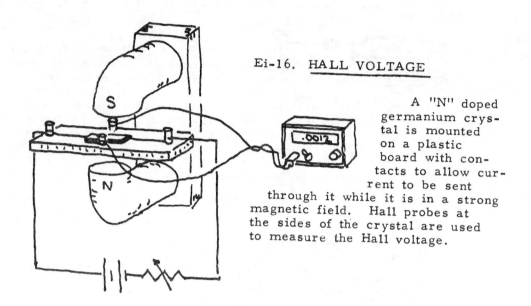

Ei-16. HALL VOLTAGE

A "N" doped germanium crystal is mounted on a plastic board with contacts to allow current to be sent through it while it is in a strong magnetic field. Hall probes at the sides of the crystal are used to measure the Hall voltage.

Ei-17. ROTATING PLASMA

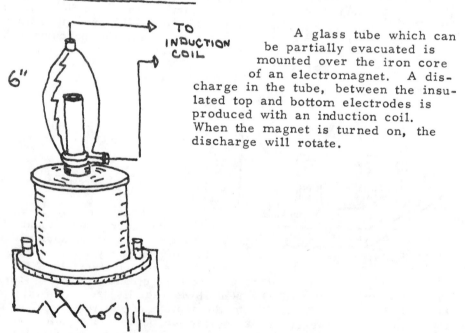

A glass tube which can be partially evacuated is mounted over the iron core of an electromagnet. A discharge in the tube, between the insulated top and bottom electrodes is produced with an induction coil. When the magnet is turned on, the discharge will rotate.

Ei-18.   FORCES ON AN ELECTRON BEAM

15"

A beam of free electrons is generated tangent to a circle about the center of a glass bulb.   The bulb is not evacuated completely, but a trace of gas is retained so that a small amount of ionization can occur along the electron beam trajectory and render the beam visible.   The ionized gas also provides gas focusing of the beam.   A uniform magnetic field is produced by a pair of Helmholtz coils arranged with their axes through the center of the bulb.   This field must be sufficiently strong to make the beam travel through a complete circle in the bulb.   The velocities of the electrons may be varied by an adjustable accelerating voltage on the power supply.   The radius of the beam is adjusted with the current through the Helmholtz coils.

4"

Ei-19.   DC MOTOR

An open model of a DC motor has its coil mounted between two poles of a large alnico magnet.   The brushes and commutator are exposed on the shaft so the student can see when the switching is made in the cycle.

4"

Ei-20.   JUMPING WIRE

Two conducting cups are filled with mercury and a bent wire dips into each of them.   The wire is in the field of a large magnet.   When current is sent in the correct direction through the wire, the wire will jump out of the magnetic field.

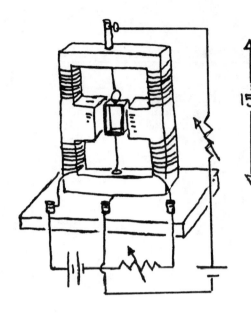

Ej-1. ELEMENTS OF A
         GALVANOMETER

A large soft iron yoke is made with
field windings in which one can vary the
field current. Separate connections are
made to a coil in the gap of the yoke.
By varying the current in the field windings and in the coil, one can show the
characteristics of a galvanometer movement. Reversing both the field and the
coil currents leave the deflection unchanged, as in an AC meter.

15"

Ej-2. GALVANOMETER WITH
           PERMANENT MAGNET

A galvanometer with a permanent magnet
has an open construction which can be
studied. This can be used only with DC.

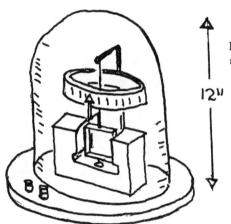

12"

Ej-3. HOT WIRE AMMETER

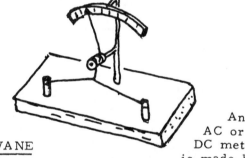

Ej-4. IRON VANE
          METER

An AC or DC
meter is made for
large currents by
having a heavy coil
surround soft iron vanes
which are movable. The
induced magnetism in the
bars makes them repel each
other, and the moving vane
deflects an amount proportional
to the current.

An
AC or
DC meter
is made by
using the linear ex-
pansion of a wire.
The amount of expan-
sion is measured by
mechanically coupling
to a pointer system.

E-36

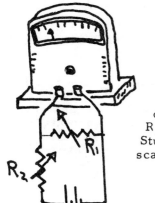

Ej-5.   SENSITIVITY AND RESISTANCE OF
GALVANOMETER

The meter movement of a demonstration galvanometer
is used as a galvanometer. With R_2 much greater than
the resistance of the galvanometer, the current is controlled almost completely by R_2. Start with R_1 at
infinity and a full scale deflection of the galvanometer.
Then decrease R_1 until the meter gives a one half full
scale deflection. The value of R_1 is then the resistance
of the galvanometer. Knowing the voltage and R_1 and
R_2, one can calculate the current for a given deflection.
Students understand the process better if one uses a full
scale deflection for the sensitivity.

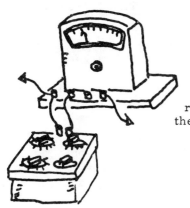

Ej-6.   CONVERTING A GALVANOMETER TO
A VOLTMETER

Knowing the resistance and sensitivity of the
galvanometer element, one calculates the resistance
necessary to convert to a voltmeter of a specified
range. The resistance is added, and the reading on
the instrument is checked against some known voltage.

Ej-7.   CONVERTING A GALVANOMETER TO
AN AMMETER

Knowing the resistance and sensitivity of the
galvanometer movement, one may calculate the
value of the shunt resistance necessary to convert
the galvanometer to an ammeter of a desired range.
If one is careful, a copper wire of known resistance
per unit length can be shunted across the galvanometer
terminals and then lengthened until the desired reading is
obtained. One must be careful to maintain good electrical
contact at all times.

Ek-1. FORCES DUE TO INDUCED CURRENTS

A light aluminum ring is suspended bifilarly as a pendulum. As a bar magnet is moved toward the ring, the magnetic field induces currents in the ring which repel it from the magnet. When the bar magnet is moved away, the ring is attracted to the magnet. One then reverses the polarity of the magnet and repeats the observations. The induced currents are created so that they always oppose the motion. Note that the forces are present only when motion is actually taking place.

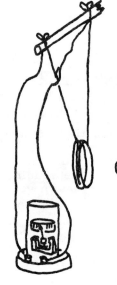

Ek-2. CURRENTS AND FORCES BY INDUCTION

The aluminum ring of the previous experiment is replaced by a flat coil with its leads connected to a galvanometer. The direction of the current can be ascertained, along with that of the force for various motions of the magnet.

Ek-3. DIRECTION OF INDUCED CURRENTS

A stationary coil is used similar to that of the previous experiment. Galvanometer deflections are measured for various motions and polarities of the magnet.

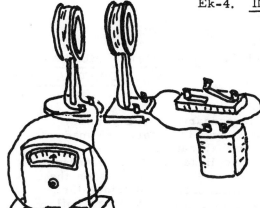

Ek-4. INDUCED CURRENTS DUE TO CHANGING CURRENTS

A primary and a secondary coil are arranged so that changing fluxes in the primary give induced currents in the secondary. The experiment shows that the induced currents always try to maintain the magnetic field that existed before the change started. The currents that are induced in the secondary exist only while the current in the primary is changing.

Ek-5. TIME INTEGRAL OF INDUCED ELECTROMAGNETIC FORCE

The primary circuit is arranged so it can make fast and slow changes of a measured current change. The secondary coil is connected to a storage oscilloscope so that the magnitude of the induced EMF may be recorded as a function of time. One can show that for a given current change in the primary, the time integral of the secondary EMF is a constant by integrating the curves.

Ek-6. EARTH INDUCTOR

The magnetic field of the Earth is measured with a large flip coil which can be turned in the Earth's field. The flux change on flipping is compared with the ballistic galvanometer deflection for a standard flux change. From the known area of the flip coil and the flux change, the Earth's magnetic field can be calculated.

STANDARD FLUX

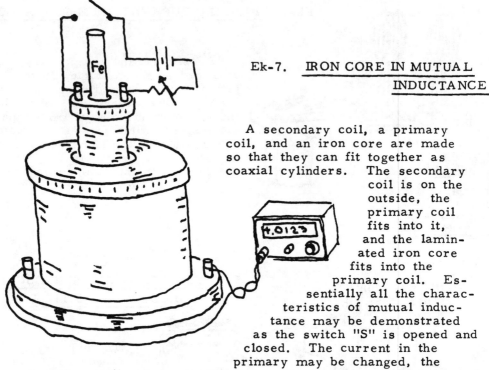

Ek-7. IRON CORE IN MUTUAL INDUCTANCE

A secondary coil, a primary coil, and an iron core are made so that they can fit together as coaxial cylinders. The secondary coil is on the outside, the primary coil fits into it, and the laminated iron core fits into the primary coil. Essentially all the characteristics of mutual inductance may be demonstrated as the switch "S" is opened and closed. The current in the primary may be changed, the geometric coupling between primary and secondary may be changed, and the amount of the iron core in the magnetic circuit may be varied.

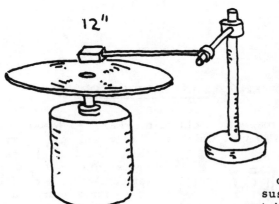

12"

E1-1. LEVITATION

A device is built which is quite similar to a record player. The "record" is a rotating disc. A small magnet suspended so it can rise freely is the "pickup". When the disc rotates, eddy currents develop which in turn create a magnetic field opposing the field of the suspended magnet. The magnet is repelled by the magnetic field and rises to ride free of the rotating disc.

E1-2. DAMPED PENDULUM

A bar magnet is suspended so that it can
swing as a pendulum, just clearing the lecture
bench at the bottom of the swing. When a copper
sheet is placed on the lecture bench, the pendulum
comes to a quick stop, due to the damping
caused by eddy currents generated in the copper.

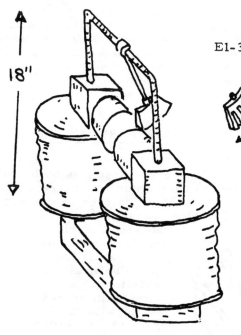

E1-3. EDDY CURRENTS IN A PENDULUM

A pendulum bob of copper
can swing freely between the
poles of a large electromagnet when the current is off.
When the magnet is on, the
pendulum comes to a quick
halt. The bob is then replaced by one of similar shape
but which has slots to prevent
the circulation of eddy currents.
This will swing freely with the magnet
on or off. The experiment may be repeated with a ring and a split ring each
serving as the bob.

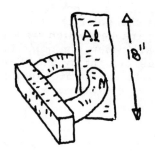

E1-4. FALLING ALUMINUM SHEET

A sheet of aluminum is allowed to fall between
the poles of a large alnico magnet. While the sheet
is between the poles, it moves very slowly.

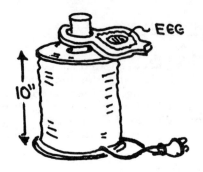

E1-5. FRYING EGG

A copper frying pan is made of heavy copper sheet. The frying pan has a hole which allows it to fit over a 1 1/4 inch stranded iron core of a large solenoid. When the solenoid is connected to 110 volts AC (or better, 220 volts AC) the alternating current will generate sufficient eddy currents in the pan to fry an egg.

E1-6. MONEY SORTER

If one has silver quarters and ersatz quarters, one can sort them by dropping them between the poles of a large alnico magnet.

A set of alnico "horns" should be mounted on a soft iron rail with grooves on the side to prevent tipping. The gap between the poles is adjustable, and the arrangement can be used in many different experiments.

Em-1. SPARK COIL

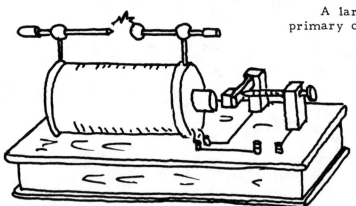

A large spark coil is built with a primary coil which can carry up to a few amperes of current. The secondary has many thousands of turns, and the ends are connected to a spark gap. The box below the coil contains a large capacitor which places the primary in approximate resonance with the inductance and stray capacitance of the secondary coil.

The spark coil should be connected so that the current can be reversed in the primary. The high voltage in the secondary develops when the current breaks in the primary. Effects of the polarity of the high voltage across the secondary coil may be studied. A spark gap which will just allow a spark when the point is positive will give no spark when the point is negative. The breakdown starts at the point, as is made evident by the direction of branching of the spark. The branches point in the direction of propagation of the leader spark.

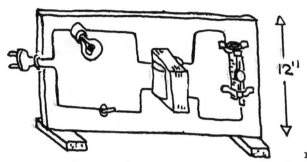

Em-2. PRIMARY CURRENT CHANGE WITH SECONDARY LOAD

A transformer is mounted on a board with a variable secondary load. The current in the primary is metered by the brightness of a lamp in series. As the current in the secondary is increased, the current in the primary increases, although there is no connection between the two circuits other than the flux linkages.

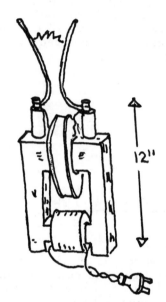

Em-3. JACOB'S LADDER

A large transformer with a 15 KV secondary has the secondary output connected to a set of vertical heavy copper "horns". At the bottom the gap is sufficiently small that a spark can jump and start an arc. The ionization then will allow the spark to jump a much larger gap as the heat convects the spark up the "horn".

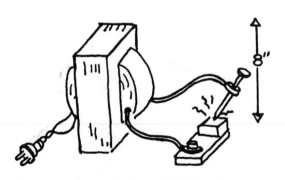

Em-4. LARGE CURRENT TRANSFORMER

A heavy transformer giving large secondary currents at low voltages is used to melt nails.

Em-5. DISSECTIBLE TRANSFORMER

Leybold sells a transformer with interchangeable secondary windings. Step-up and step-down voltages may be obtained with the same primary winding.

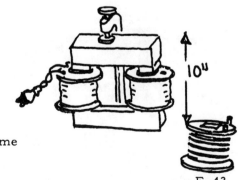

E-43

Em-6. PHONY HEALTH BELT

The instructor has both the primary and an isolated secondary of a transformer around him. The secondary coil has a light bulb to indicate current flow. He "takes" an "iron" pill and the secondary light glows. The instructor must let the secondary coil fall surreptitiously as he "takes" the pill to create the desired effect.

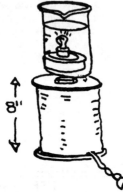

Em-7. LIGHT UNDER WATER

A small flashlight bulb is attached to a coil. The arrangement is well waxed so it will not short out when it is under water. The light and coil are placed in a beaker of water which is set on an iron core induction coil. When the induction coil is connected to a source of AC power, the light glows under water.

Em-8. <u>INDUCTION COIL</u>

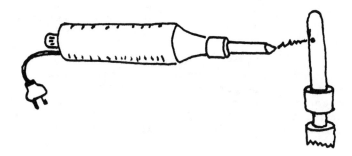

A 110 volt induction coil (Cenco) produces sparks about one inch long. A test tube with a small leak may be evacuated and one can demonstrate that the spark finds the lower pressure in the region of the leak.

Em-9. <u>SHOCKER</u>

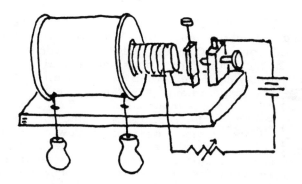

The primary of an induction coil is switched on and off with a slow vibrator. The secondary coil can slide varying amounts over the primary while the operator hangs on to two metal handles. He tests his ability to take electric shocks by seeing how far he can slide the secondary over the primary and still maintain his grip on the handles.

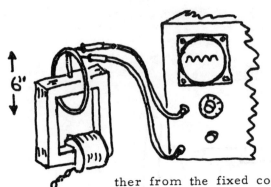

Em-10. SINGLE TURN TRANSFORMER

A transformer is built with a single turn on the secondary short-circuited to form a ring. An oscilloscope is then used to measure the voltage between arbitrary points on the ring. One contact is held fixed and the other is slid along the ring. As the moving contact separates further from the fixed contact, the voltage indicated on the oscilloscope gets larger also, even maintaining a large value when the contacts are touching after one turn. The phenomenon continues after more turns. One should explain the phenomenon by having the students watch the configuration of the measuring leads.

Em-11. INDUCED EMF

A transformer has a small gap through which a loose wire may be moved to divide various cross-sectional areas of the gap. The oscilloscope is first connected from one side and then without moving the wire, the 'scope is connected from the other side. The voltage will be different even though the wire is in the same position in both measurements.

Em-12. JUMPING RING

A large inductor has an iron core which extends from the top. An aluminum ring slides over the extended core. When the inductor is connected to an AC power source, the ring jumps into the air. The ring may then be cooled in liquid nitrogen and the experiment repeated. The ring will now jump much higher. The cooling lowers the resistance of the ring and allows more current to flow as well as altering the phase shift more favorably for continued repulsive forces. The result must be discussed in terms of the relative inductance and the reactance of the ring.

Em-13. ROTATING BALL

A hollow aluminum sphere rides on a watch glass placed on the gap of a transformer which has only a primary winding. The gap has what is known as a "shaded pole", made by cutting an additional gap in the transformer core and winding a short circuited band of heavy copper around part of the pole face. The shaded pole makes an out-of-phase component of the magnetic field and hence gives a rotating magnetic field which induces currents in the aluminum ball serving as the armature of an induction motor.

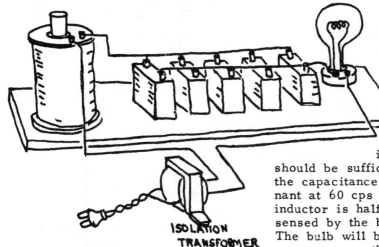

ISOLATION
TRANSFORMER

En-1. SERIES L-R-C
CIRCUIT

An inductance, a
capacitance, and a
large light bulb (low
resistance) are con-
nected in series to
the output of an isolat-
ion transformer. There
should be sufficient capacitance so that
the capacitance and inductance are resonant at 60 cps when the iron core of the
inductor is halfway out. The current is
sensed by the brightness of the light bulb.
The bulb will burn most brightly at the
resonance as the iron core is moved inward or outward.

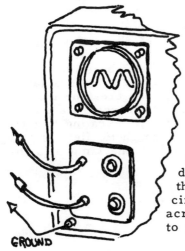

GROUND

En-2. PHASE SHIFT IN AN
L-R-C CIRCUIT

An oscilloscope with a dual input is connected
across various components of the L-R-C circuit
described above. The isolation transformer allows
the ground connection to be made anywhere in the
circuit. One can then compare the phase of voltages
across various components as the inductor is varied
to pass through resonance.

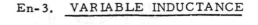

En-3. VARIABLE INDUCTANCE

An inductance with a moveable iron
core is in series with a light bulb. As
the core is moved out or in, the light bulb
burns brighter or dimmer.

En-4.   CAPACITIVE IMPEDANCE

A capacitor and a light bulb are connected in series. The capacitor may be left in the circuit, or shorted, to show the effect of adding capacity in series.

En-5.   CURRENT IN AN INDUCTIVE CIRCUIT

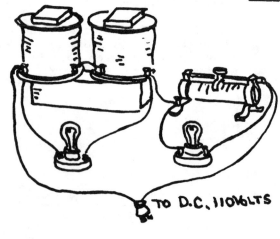

TO D.C. 110VOLTS

A large magnet is connected in series with a rheostat. Light bulbs serve as voltmeters across the magnet and the rheostat. When the apparatus is connected to a DC power source, the bulb across the magnet flashes brightly at first, and then becomes dimmer, showing the change of current through the inductance. Subsequently, the lamp across the rheostat burns brightly when the current has built to a large steady value. On breaking the circuit a bright flash occurs across the magnet lamp, indicating that the energy of the magnetic field is being dissipated in the lamp bulb load.

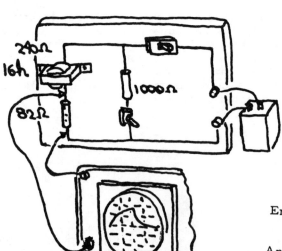

En-6.   R-L TIME CONSTANT

An inductance is in series with a small resistance so that voltages across the resistor and therefore currents through the inductor may be measured. The rise of the current is observed with an oscilloscope as a battery is applied to the inductor. A second resistor is connected across the arrangement, so that the decay of the current can also be observed when the battery is removed.

E-48

En-7. TIME CONSTANT OF AN INDUCTIVE CIRCUIT

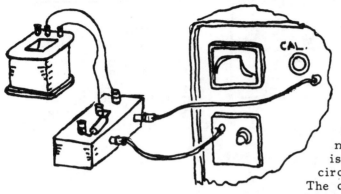

A 1000 turn coil
(such as that manufactured
by Leybold) is connected
in series with a 10 ohm
resistance. The square
wave calibration signal
from the oscilloscope at a
magnitude of about 2 volts
is placed across the two
circuit elements in series.
The output of the circuit is measured across the resistor. The circuit should be used with a storage oscilloscope. Traces are made first
with the air core, next with the
coil placed on the iron yoke,
and finally with the coil on a
closed iron yoke. The steps
may be repeated using half
of the turns on the coil.
(The Leybold coil has connections which allow one to use
either the full number of turns
or half the full number.)

En-8. TIME CONSTANT OF A CAPACITIVE CIRCUIT

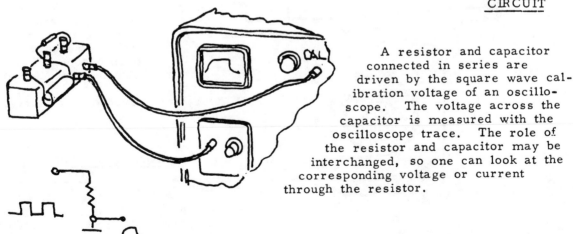

A resistor and capacitor
connected in series are
driven by the square wave calibration voltage of an oscilloscope. The voltage across the
capacitor is measured with the
oscilloscope trace. The role of
the resistor and capacitor may be
interchanged, so one can look at the
corresponding voltage or current
through the resistor.

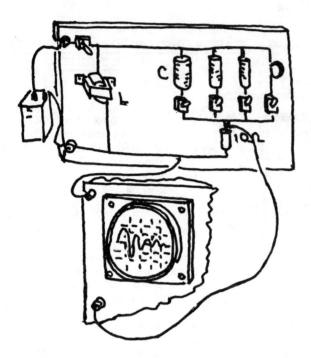

En-9. RINGING CIRCUIT

A battery is connected and disconnected from an L-C parallel circuit with a small resistance in series
for monitoring the current. Various
size capacitors may be switched in or
out of the circuit. As the capacity is
changed, one observes a change in the
characteristic frequency of the circuit.

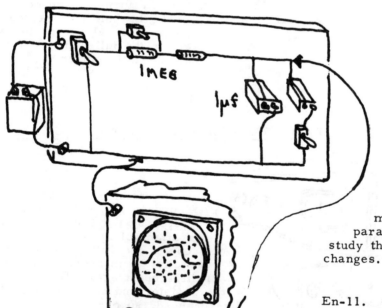

En-10. RC TIME
CONSTANT

A double pole, single
throw switch either con-
nects a battery to a res-
istance and capacitance
in series or discharges
the capacitance through
the resistance. The
growth and decay of the
voltage across the capac-
itance is measured with
an oscilloscope. The 'scope
may also be connected in
parallel with the resistance to
study the corresponding voltage
changes.

En-11. LONG R-C TIME
CONSTANT

A 120 volt DC supply is connected
to a 5600 µf   electrolytic capacitor
through a light bulb. The bulb gets
dimmer as the capacitor charges.
The capacitor may then be disconnected from the supply, and discharged through the bulb, in which
case the bulb again gets dimmer
as time progresses.

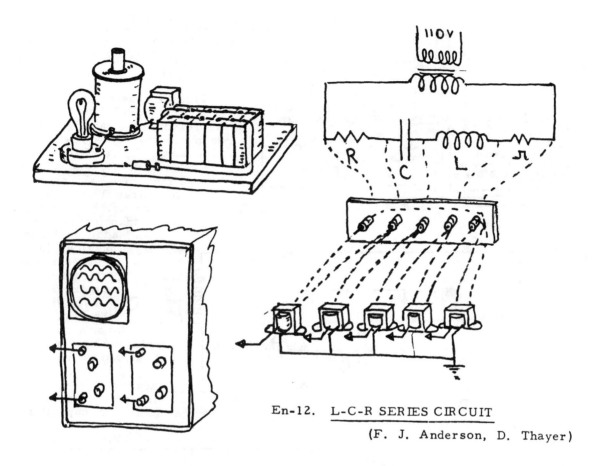

En-12. L-C-R SERIES CIRCUIT

(F. J. Anderson, D. Thayer)

This a modification of En-1.   A variable inductance, a large lamp
serving as resistance, a bank of capacitors, and a small resistance for
measuring currents are connected in series across an isolation transformer.
Any point of the series circuit may be grounded so that an oscilloscope can
be used to display the voltage across any component.   However it is often
useful to measure simultaneously the voltage across the different circuit
components to help the students understand the phase relationships.   Since
one cannot ground two points of the circuit at the same time, a further
modification is made by placing a small 6 volt transformer across each
component.   The low voltage windings of each transformer may then be
connected to the oscilloscope simultaneously.   One may then display all the
voltages at once, with the proper phase shifts, on a dual beam four channel
oscilloscope.   (The 6 volt transformers loaded by an oscilloscope have such
a high impedance that the characteristic current and voltage of any component
in the series circuit is not altered.)   The inductance is varied by pulling out
a movable iron core.   The number of capacitors may be varied by a set of
switches.

En-13. PARALLEL RESONANCE
(D. Thayer)

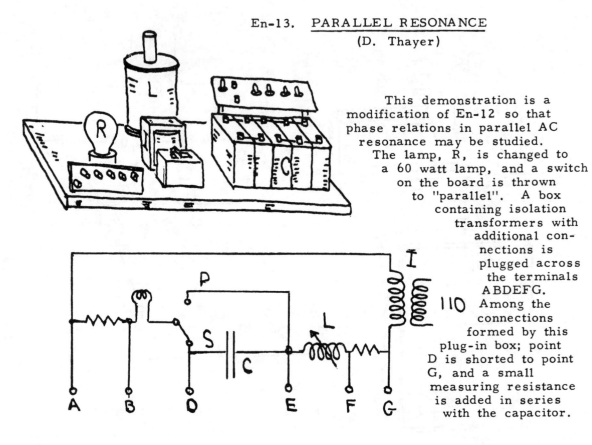

This demonstration is a modification of En-12 so that phase relations in parallel AC resonance may be studied.

The lamp, R, is changed to a 60 watt lamp, and a switch on the board is thrown to "parallel". A box containing isolation transformers with additional connections is plugged across the terminals ABDEFG. Among the connections formed by this plug-in box; point D is shorted to point G, and a small measuring resistance is added in series with the capacitor.

The final circuit then appears as shown in the second circuit diagram. One can use a dual beam ocsilloscope with dual traces to show; the applied voltage, the total current, the current through the inductance, and the current through the capacitance. The vector addition of the currents with all of the phase relations can be shown. If one starts with maximum inductance and capacitance, the circuit is off resonance. As either L or C is decreased the circuit approaches resonance, and the large circulating currents in the "tank" circuit are shown to be much greater than the total current.

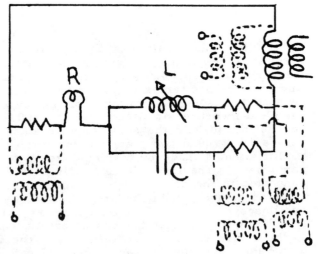

Eo-1. OHM'S LAW*

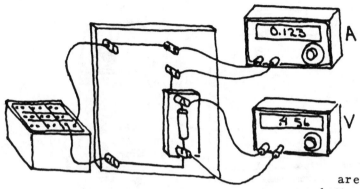

Eo-2. KIRCHOFF'S
VOLTAGE LAW*

Variable voltages
are selected at the
battery pack.   The
voltage across the resistor
and the current through the
resistor are read with digital
meters.

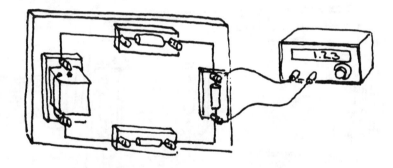

A 1.5 volt battery and 3 resistors are plugged into the board
in series.   The digital voltmeter readings show that the sum of
the voltage gains equals the sum of the voltage drops.   Resistors
may be replaced by other batteries.

*   The following experiments were constructed by Phil Johnson
(School of Physics, U. of Minn.) and designed to give maximum
versatility with minimum time for changes.   An effort was made
to show the relations between circuit diagrams and working
components.

Eo-3. VOLTAGE DIVIDER*

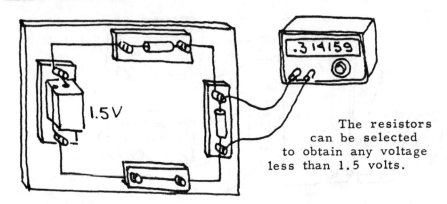

The resistors
can be selected
to obtain any voltage
less than 1.5 volts.

Eo-4. CONTINUITY OF CURRENT*

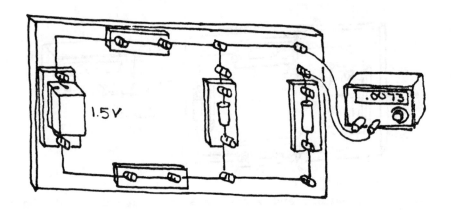

    The ammeter is inserted into the circuit at various points
to show the current is continuous at any junction. The same
arrangement can be used to show how the current in any branch
of the circuit can be related to the voltage and conductance.

Eo-5. EQUIVALENT SERIES RESISTANCE *

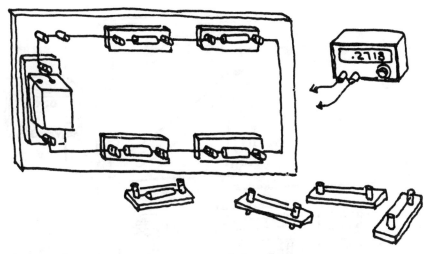

    A set of resistors is   arranged in series.
An equivalent resistor is then plugged into the circuit
in their place.   The meter may be used to show the voltage and
current from the battery are the same for the equivalent resistor
as for the set of resistors it replaced.

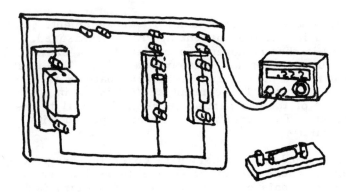

Eo-6.   EQUIVALENT PARALLEL RESISTANCE*

    Resistors are arranged in parallel.   They are then replaced
by the equivalent resistance.   The meter is used to show that
the current and voltage from the battery is the same in each case.

Eo-7. SUPERPOSITION OF CURRENTS *

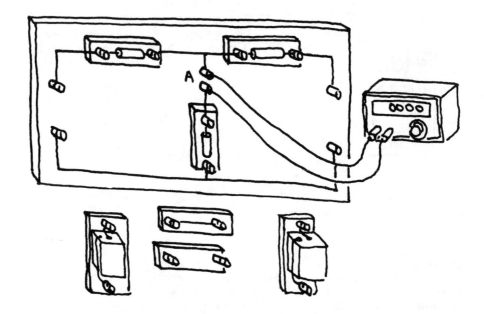

Several resistors are connected in a "T" arrangement. Both batteries are plugged in and the current at "A" is measured. One of the batteries is then removed and replaced by a short-circuit bar. The current is again measured at "A". The first battery is returned to the circuit and the second battery is replaced by a shorting bar. The current at "A" is again measured. The sum of the two partial currents is equal to the original total current. The experiment may be repeated with different battery polarities.

One can easily extend the discussion to cover the reciprocity theorem. The points where the batteries are connected are considered as four terminals of a "black box". A battery is used at one set of terminals and an ammeter is connected across the other. The battery and the ammeter are then interchanged.

Eo-8. WHEATSTONE BRIDGE*

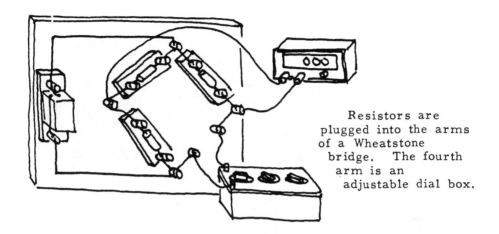

Resistors are
plugged into the arms
of a Wheatstone
bridge.   The fourth
arm is an
adjustable dial box.

Eo-9. IMPEDANCE BRIDGE*

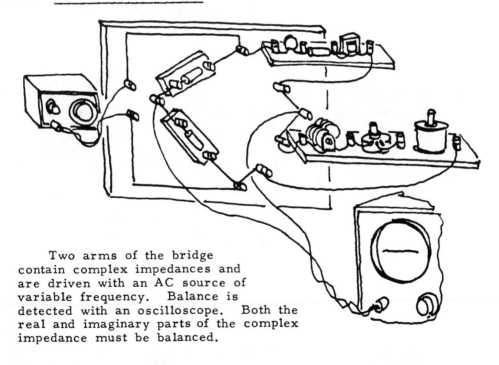

Two arms of the bridge
contain complex impedances and
are driven with an AC source of
variable frequency.   Balance is
detected with an oscilloscope.   Both the
real and imaginary parts of the complex
impedance must be balanced.

Eo-10. BRIDGE RECTIFIER*

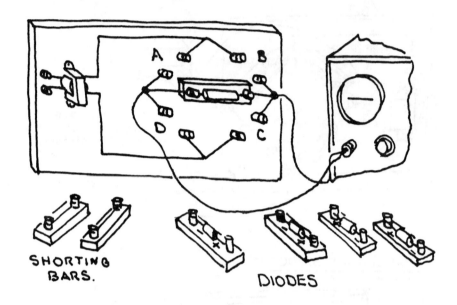

SHORTING
BARS.

DIODES

A 12 volt transformer drives the bridge. First, place
shorting bars at "A" and "C" and show the sine wave voltage.
Second, replace the shorting bar at "A" with a diode and show
half wave rectification. Third, do the same experiment using
"B" and "D" with "A" and "C" open. This time reverse the
diode. Now place forward diodes at "A" and "C" and reverse
diodes at "B" and "D" to show full wave rectification. Finally
have a forward diode at "A", a reverse diode at "B", and place
capacitors at "C" and "D" to get a DC voltage.

Eo-11. L/R TIME CONSTANT*

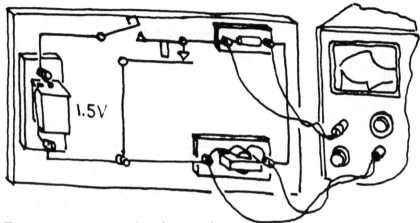

     The time constant is observed
both on energizing and de-energizing the circuit. The voltages
across the resistor and the inductor are observed with a dual
trace oscilloscope. The special switch makes the circuit while
the shorting wire is still connected. Further depression of the
switch opens the shorting wire. This arrangement eliminates
sparking of the switch.

Eo-12. RC TIME CONSTANT*

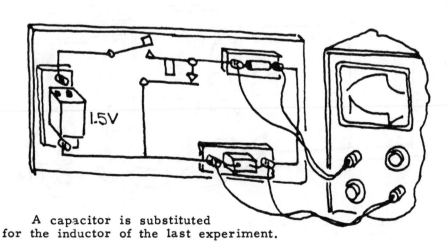

     A capacitor is substituted
for the inductor of the last experiment.

Eo-13. CHARACTERISTIC TIMES IN A SERIES L-R-C CIRCUIT*

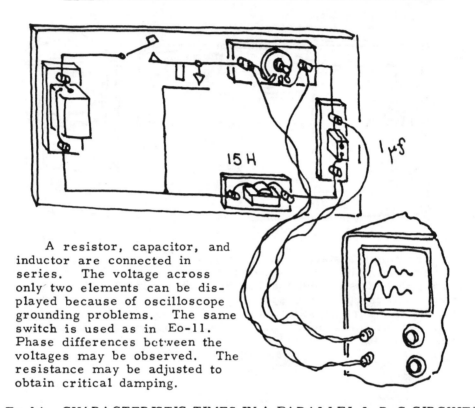

A resistor, capacitor, and inductor are connected in series. The voltage across only two elements can be displayed because of oscilloscope grounding problems. The same switch is used as in Eo-11. Phase differences between the voltages may be observed. The resistance may be adjusted to obtain critical damping.

Eo-14. CHARACTERISTIC TIMES IN A PARALLEL L-R-C CIRCUIT*

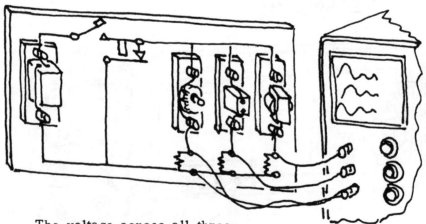

The voltage across all three elements may be displayed showing the phase shifts. The resistance may be decreased until critical damping is observed.

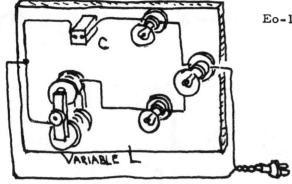

Eo-15.   PARALLEL AC RESONANCE

A capacitor and variable inductor are selected so that they can be tuned to resonance at 60 cps. A lamp is then placed in series with each to monitor the current in each branch. The two branches are in parallel and then in series with a third light bulb which monitors the entire current. As the variable inductor is tuned from the largest to the smallest value, the current shifts from the capacitive branch to the inductive branch. At resonance, the bulbs in each branch glow brightly while the bulb in series with the line is unlit. This shows the vector nature of the circulating currents in the parallel resonant circuit.

Ep-1.   MARX GENERATOR

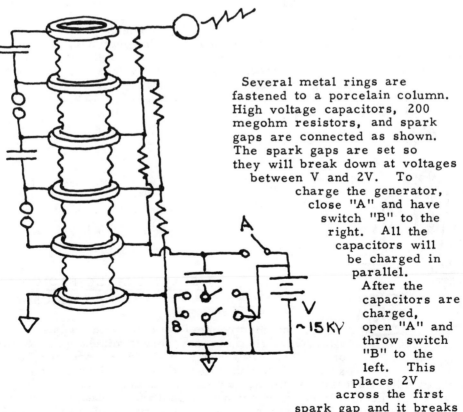

Several metal rings are fastened to a porcelain column. High voltage capacitors, 200 megohm resistors, and spark gaps are connected as shown. The spark gaps are set so they will break down at voltages between V and 2V.   To charge the generator, close "A" and have switch "B" to the right.   All the capacitors will be charged in parallel.

After the capacitors are charged, open "A" and throw switch "B" to the left.   This places 2V across the first spark gap and it breaks down. Since the resistance is now low, the next capacitor adds the voltage V which breaks down the next spark gap, etc. During the breakdown, the voltages across all of the capacitors are added to give a high voltage.

Ep-2. TESLA COIL

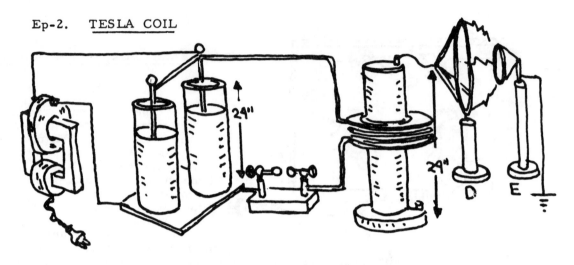

A 15 kilovolt, 60 cps transformer is connected across a set of Leyden jars which have at least 1/4" glass walls. The Leyden jars in turn are in parallel with the 10 turn primary winding of the high frequency transformer. In the parallel connection there is, however, a spark gap which breaks down at 15 kilovolts and thus becomes conducting to the high frequency current. The inductance of the primary winding of the high frequency coil and the capacitance of the Leyden jars should have a resonant frequency of about 500 kilocycles. The wires must all be made of heavy power wire so that large currents can resonate. The secondary winding of the high frequency transformer has many thousands of turns, and is oil immersed. At the output of the secondary, one has high frequency, high voltage power available. If the frequency of the system is very high, one will have mostly corona and few sparks, as sparks do not have sufficient time to propagate under these conditions. If the frequency is as low as 500 kilocycles, one can develop long sparks. The lower frequency is usually realized with larger components.

Ep-3. SPACE CHARGE FROM HIGH
FREQUENCY CORONA

The electrodes D and E of the Tesla coil are operated to give high frequency corona discharge. A fan placed to one side blows the air in the discharge over a charged electroscope. When the electroscope is initially charged negatively, it will rapidly discharge when the fan is turned on, indicating that the space charge from the high frequency corona is positive. (The corona is not electrons going into the air.) If the electroscope is positively charged, it will not discharge.

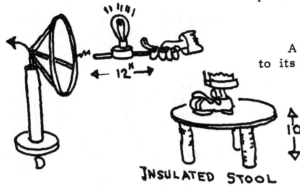

Ep-4. HIGH FREQUENCY CURRENTS

A light bulb with two antennae attached to its terminals is held by the instructor while he stands on a well insulated stool. The capacity of the instructor is sufficient at the Tesla coil frequency to give enough current to light the bulb. The skin effect keeps all currents at the surface of the body.

Ep-5. FLUORESCENT LIGHT BULB IN RADIATION FIELD

A fluorescent light bulb in the proximity of the Tesla coil will light up in the radiation field.

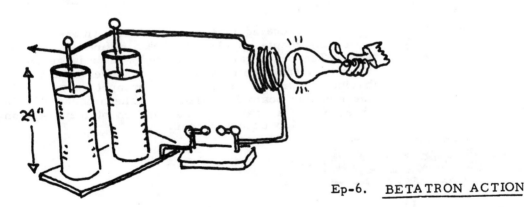

Ep-6. BETATRON ACTION

The high frequency transformer is removed from the Tesla coil and the primary of the transformer is replaced by a few turns of inductive winding to form a flat 6 inch diameter coil. A partially evacuated glass bulb is then brought in along the axis of the coil. The changing magnetic flux through the bulb yields an EMF around the axis of the coil which is sufficiently large to ionize the gas in the bulb. The electrons have short mean free paths, but the combination of the magnetic field and gas focussing gives a visible beam in the tube.

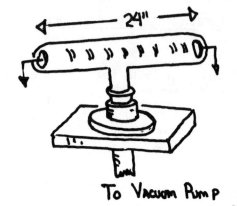

Ep-7. CROOKES TUBE

A glass tube is evacuated while there is a high DC voltage between a pair of electrodes sealed into the ends of the tube. As the amount of air in the tube decreases, the mean free path of the electrons increases until avalanching can take place. The tube then starts to glow with many characteristic patterns as the pressure continues to decrease. The accumulation of space charge in various regions gives the high electric fields where electron avalanching can take place. The high voltage may be supplied by a spark coil since the spark coil gives a much larger voltage on the breaking than on the making of the primary circuit. It therefore provides an essentially DC voltage for the discharge.

To Vacuum Pump

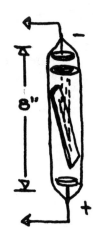 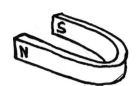

Ep-8. BENDING OF AN ELECTRON BEAM

An evacuated tube has an oblique fluorescent screen which intercepts an electron beam defined by a small slit. The beam can be produced with a large DC voltage or with a spark coil as described above. When a magnet having the proper orientation is brought up to the device, the electron beam is deflected. The amount of deflection is shown by a change in the position of the beam on the fluorescent screen.

Ep-9. PADDLEWHEEL

An electron beam between two electrodes in an evacuated vessel is intercepted by a paddle wheel on two glass rails. The electron beam transfers its momentum to the paddle wheel and turns it to make it roll on the rails. A spark coil may be used as the source of high voltage.

Ep-10. MALTESE CROSS

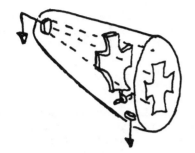

A tiltable metal shield in the form of a cross
is in an evacuated tube which has a fluorescent
screen near the anode.   The electron beam
produces a shadow of the cross on the screen.

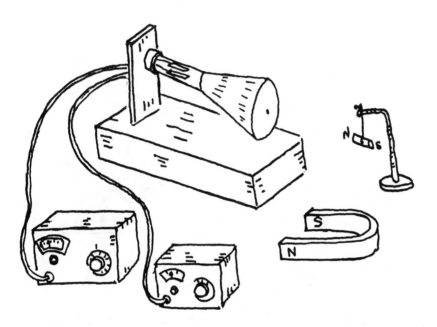

Ep-11. e/m FOR ELECTRONS

A cheap oscilloscope tube is mounted openly so that the distance between the
deflection plates can be measured.   Auxiliary power supplies furnish the accelerating voltage and the deflecting voltage, which can be measured with meters.
A weak horseshoe magnet provides a magnetic field transverse to the beam direction and the electric deflecting field.   The deflecting field is determined from
the deflection voltage and the distance between the deflecting plates.   The
velocity of the electrons is determined from the measured accelerating voltage.
The magnetic field is found with a small magnet suspended on a torsionless
thread.   The rate of oscillation is found with the horseshoe magnet and then with
some known magnetic field, such as the Earth's field.   The experiment gives an
order of magnitude answer for e/m.

Ep-12. RADIATION FROM A DIPOLE

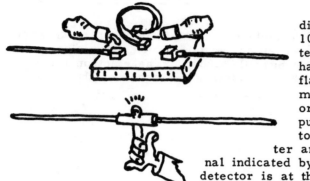

A vacuum tube oscillator drives a dipole antenna at a frequency of about 100 megacycles. The radiation is detected with a second dipole antenna having two metal stubs connected by a flashlight bulb. The detector stubs are made so that they are telescoping in order to tune the detector to the output of the oscillator. When the detector antenna is parallel to the transmitter and to one side, there is a strong signal indicated by a bright glow of the bulb. If the detector is at the side, but with the antenna at 90° to the transmitter, there is no signal. There is no signal for any orientation of the antenna if the detector is placed at the ends of the radiator. The signal on the sides falls off inversely as the square of the distance between the transmitter and receiver.

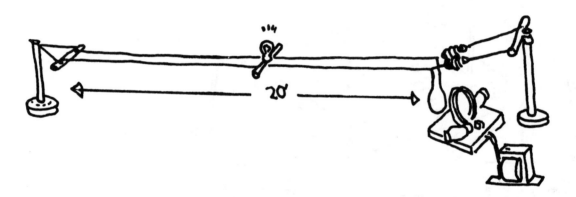

Ep-13. LECHER WIRES

The high frequency oscillator described in the previous experiment has its dipole radiator antennae removed and the one turn inductive coil of the oscillator is mutually coupled to a turn of copper wire which feeds two parallel wires stretched across the lecture room. Standing waves are developed on the parallel wires by varying the lengths of the wires to obtain optimum tuning with the oscillator. An incandescent or neon lamp connected to a set of metal stubs which can be slid along the parallel wires serves as the detector. At intervals of $\lambda/2$ the bulb will light, and it will be extinguished at other points.

E-66

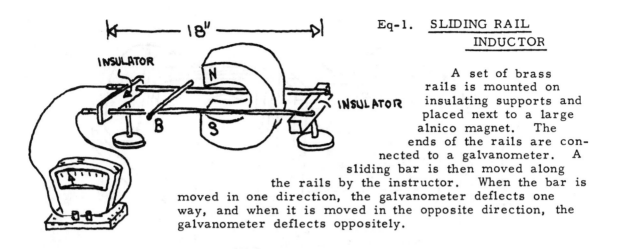

Eq-1. SLIDING RAIL
        INDUCTOR

A set of brass
rails is mounted on
insulating supports and
placed next to a large
alnico magnet.   The
ends of the rails are connected to a galvanometer.   A
sliding bar is then moved along
the rails by the instructor.   When the bar is
moved in one direction, the galvanometer deflects one
way, and when it is moved in the opposite direction, the
galvanometer deflects oppositely.

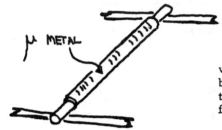

Eq-2. μ -METAL SHIELD

The sliding bar of the last experiment is
wrapped in a μ metal shield and moved as
before.   The magnitude of the deflections is
the same as before, even though no lines of
force can now penetrate the bar.

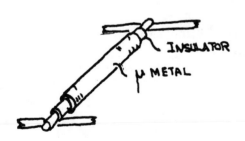

Eq-3. μ -METAL SHIELD AND
        INSULATOR

This experiment is similar to the last
one except that insulating material is now
placed between the sliding rod and the μ
metal shield.   The deflections of the galvanometer are still unaltered.

Eq-4. <u>MOTOR GENERATOR</u>

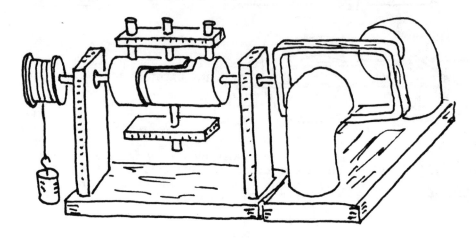

A large flat coil is placed so it can rotate between the poles of a large Alnico magnet. The armature has both slip rings and a commutator. Both alternating and direct current voltages can be obtained when the device is operated as a generator. The coil is driven by a falling weight. If current is provided to the commutator, the device runs as a motor and winds up the weight.

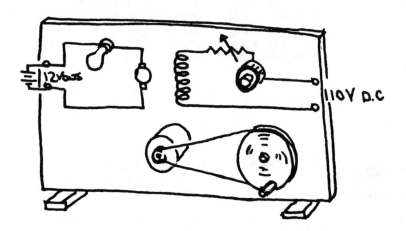

Eq-5. <u>MOTOR-GENERATOR</u>

A DC motor is connected so that the armature and field coils can be seperately excited. A light bulb is placed in series with the armature to indicate current flow. When the motor starts, the bulb burns brightly and then becomes dimmer as the motor comes to speed showing that a back EMF develops. The motor is connected to a pulley which can now be cranked by the instructor. If the land cranking aids the motor, the light will eventually extinguish. If the cranking is continued at a much higher speed, the bulb starts to glow again while the battery becomes charged by the back EMF. The motor is now acting as a generator.

E-68

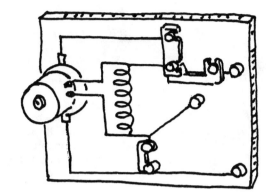

Eq-6. <u>SERIES AND PARALLEL</u>
<u>MOTORS</u>

A D.C. motor is
mounted on a board
where one may connect
the armature and field
either in series or
parallel. The running
characteristics of the
motor with the two
types of connections can
be shown.

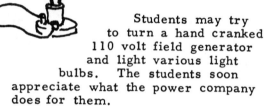

Eq-7. <u>HAND CRANKED</u>
<u>GENERATOR</u>

Students may try
to turn a hand cranked
110 volt field generator
and light various light
bulbs. The students soon
appreciate what the power company
does for them.

Er-1. <u>INTERACTION OF PERMANENT</u>
<u>MAGNET AND COIL</u>

A solenoid is suspended by contacts in mercury cups so that it
is free to move about a vertical
axis. A bar magnet is mounted
on a stand in such a way that the
magnet can rotate about a vertical
axis. The polarity of the magnet
can be studied with respect to the current flow in the coil by showing the ex-
istance of repulsive and attractive forces.

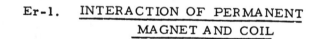

Er-2. <u>INTERACTION BETWEEN</u>
<u>BAR MAGNETS</u>

Two bar magnets are suspended on
stands which allow them to rotate about
vertical axes. The forces of attraction between unlike poles and repulsion between like poles
can be easily shown.

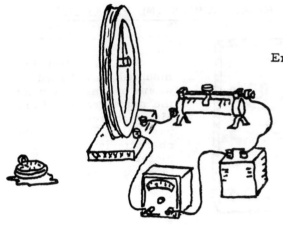

Er-3. PERIOD OF A BAR MAGNET

A short bar magnet is suspended on the axis of a flat coil by a tor-sionless string. The magnet will oscillate in the field of the coil. The current and hence the field of the coil are proportional to the square of the frequency of oscillation of the bar magnet.

Er-4. FIELD OF A MAGNET

A piece of glass sheet is placed over a bar magnet and iron filings are sprinkled onto the sheet. The filings align themselves along the field lines. The single magnet may be replaced by combinations of bar magnets and restudied.

Er-5. LODESTONE

A piece of magnetite (Fe_3O_4) ore is suspended in a magnetic field. The magnetite piece will orient itself with its magnetic axis parallel to the field. Pieces of lodestone will attract each other and iron filings.

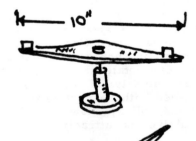

Er-6. COMPASS

A compass is used to define magnetic poles and to find the declination of the Earth's mag-netic field.

Er-7. DIP NEEDLE

A dip needle is used to determine the inclination of the Earth's magnetic field.

E-70

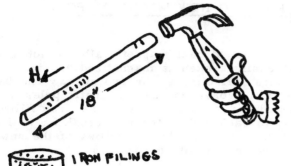

Er-8. MAGNETIZATION IN THE EARTH'S FIELD

A soft iron bar is hammered in the Earth's magnetic field and becomes magnetic. This can be tested with a compass or with iron filings.

I RON FILINGS

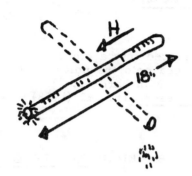

Er-9. PERMALLOY BAR

A permalloy bar held parallel to the Earth's magnetic field will hold iron filings. When it is turned through 90° so it is normal to the Earth's field, the iron filings fall off.

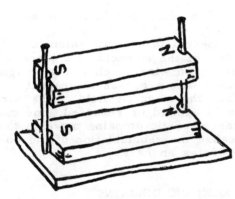

Er-10. MAGNETIC SUSPENSION

Each member of a pair of alnico magnets has notches in its ends so it can follow a vertical guide rail. With like poles over one another, the magnetic forces will suspend the top magnet. It should be pointed out that mechanical forces are necessary for stability.

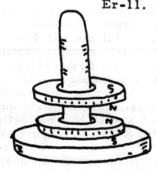

Er-11. LEVITATION OF MAGNETIC DISCS

Discs of magnetized iron alloy are held in vertical alignment by slipping the discs over a test tube. The discs are magnetized parallel to their axis of symmetry and placed over the test tube with poles in opposition. The top disc can then be bounced in a stable way above the other disc.

Er-12. FORMING NEW MAGNETIC POLES

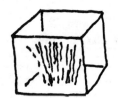

A rod of cast magnetic alloy which can be easily broken is magnetized and iron filings will cling at the two ends. The bar is then broken and new magnetic poles are created, as seen by the fact that iron filings will cling to each end of the new break as well as to the original poles. The polarities of the new poles can be tested with a compass.

Er-13. MAGNETIC MONOPOLE

Iron filings are placed into a clear casting resin and placed onto the pole of a magnet while the resin hardens. See B. Eaton, Phys. Teach. 16, 240 (1978).

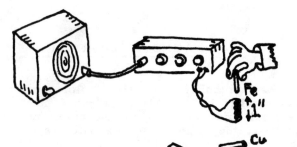

Es-1. BARKHAUSEN EFFECT

The input to a high gain audio amplifier which drives a speaker is connected to a small solenoid. The core of the solenoid is a piece of soft iron wire which can be magnetized with a horseshoe magnet. When the magnetic field at the wire core is applied or reversed, one can hear the magnetic domains move in the core because the reorientation of the domains generates an EMF.

Es-2. MAGNETIC DOMAINS

Plastic sheets are separated by many "compass-like" needles between them. All the needles can turn freely about a vertical axis. The first set has soft iron unmagnetized needles, which have random orientations. The second set of sheets has magnetized needles which arrange themselves in domains. Both sets may be displayed on an overhead projector, and both sets will have all the needles aligned in an external magnetic field.

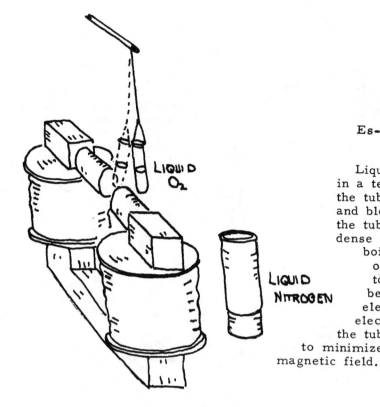

Es-3. PARAMAGNETISM

Liquid oxygen is prepared
in a test tube by immersing
the tube into liquid nitrogen
and blowing air or oxygen into
the tube. (Oxygen will con-
dense at the liquid nitrogen
boiling point.) The tube
of oxygen is suspended
to one side of the gap
between poles of a large
electromagnet. When the
electromagnet is turned on,
the tube swings into the gap
to minimize the energy in the
magnetic field.

Es-4. PARAMAGNETISM

Paramagnetic substances
such as $CuSO_4$ crystals or
bismuth crystals are suspended
in a strong magnetic field. An
energy minimum is obtained
when the long axis of the crystal
is parallel to the field. The
crystals alone will not pick up iron filings or attract each other.

Es-5. MAGNETIC FORCE

Two soft iron yokes are made with
polished pole faces so they fit together well.
A winding is placed on one yoke and a weight
pan on the other. If there is no current
through the winding, the yokes will not stick
together. The winding is then connected to a
small flashlight battery to supply current, and the
second yoke now sticks very tightly to the upper
one. Many kilograms may be added to the weight
pan and the yokes will still stick. When the battery is removed, the system collapses.

E-73

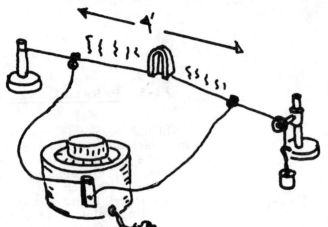

Es-6. CURIE POINT

A piece of soft iron wire is suspended between two supports. The tension is held constant by means of a pulley and weight. A horseshoe magnet is then used to pull the center of the wire upward by magnetic forces. Current is then passed through the wire until it becomes red hot and the wire loses its magnetic properties. The wire will fall free of the magnet.

Es-7. PHASE CHANGE IN IRON

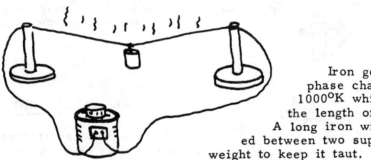

Iron goes through a phase change at about $1000^{\circ}K$ which will change the length of an iron wire. A long iron wire is suspended between two supports with a weight to keep it taut. The wire is heated by passing current through it from a Variac. The wire suddenly sags much more at the phase change. As the wire cools, there is a sudden tightening of the wire. The experiment can be shown by projection.

Es-8. CURIE TEMPERATURE

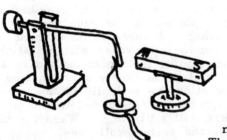

A soft iron wire is mounted with a counterweight onto a pivot so that the counterweight is a little heavier than the iron wire. A magnet will attract the wire and bring it down into a hot flame where the wire is heated to the Curie point. Without the magnetic force, the wire is lifted out of the flame where it cools and again becomes magnetic. The magnet then pulls it into the flame again. The system will oscillate as a relaxation oscillator.

Es-9. MAGNET AND NON-MAGNET

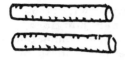

Two identical iron bars are present-ed. One of the bars is a magnet and the other is soft iron. The student is asked for an experimental procedure to determine which bar is which.

Es-10. HYSTERESIS LOOP

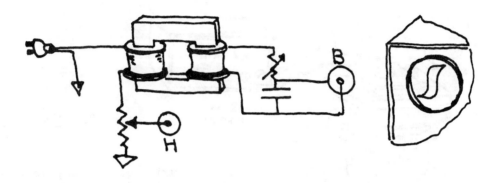

The signal "H" is placed on the horizontal input of an oscilloscope. The signal "B" in the secondary is placed on the vertical input. The hysteresis curve for the core material is then seen on the oscilloscope.

Es-11. MAGNETIC HOLDING WITH A SMALL BATTERY

A well closed (care-fully fitted iron surfaces) magnetic circuit is made with cylindrical symmetry. A coil around the inside core is excited by current from a small flashlight battery. The end yoke is provided with a weight-holder which may hold several kilograms. The load will crash to the floor when the battery is disconnected.

Et-1.   THERMOCOUPLE

A thermocouple is made by soldering iron and copper wires together to form two iron-copper junctions.   The two copper leads are connected to a galvanometer.   One junction is placed in ice water and the other is held in a flame, giving a galvanometer reading proportional to the temperature difference of the junctions. The roles of the two junctions may be reversed, and the reading on the galvanometer will reverse.

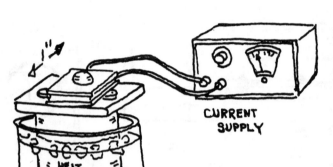

CURRENT SUPPLY

Et-2.   THERMOELECTRIC
COOLER

Thermoelectric coolers may be purchased. The bottom of the cooler is attached to a heat sink of ice water and the top may be placed in contact with the object from which it is desired to remove heat, say a drop of water.   The thermoelectric cooler will require a DC current of 5 to 10 amps at 2 to 5 volts.   The power requirements are most easily met with a variable power supply.   It is interesting to supercool water in this experiment.

Et-3.   THERMOCOUPLE
MAGNET

A heavy copper bar is wound in a single turn on a core of soft iron. The copper is shorted by a section of iron so that the circuit forms a thermocouple.   Copper "ears" are soldered to the thermocouple at the junctions so that one junction may be placed in dry ice and the other junction heated with a flame.   A soft iron plate then fits against the bottom of the enclosing iron yoke.   A weight pan and several kilogram weights may be suspended by magnetic forces when one junction of the thermocouple is heated and the other is cooled. The iron yoke must form a good closed path for the magnetic flux.

E-76

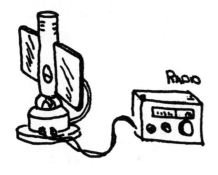

Et-4.   3M AZTEC LAMP

The 3M Company has developed a thermocouple which operates between the temperature of a kerosene lamp flame and the temperature of the cooling fins. The current from the thermocouple passes through a converter and produces sufficent voltage to power a transistor radio. The radio can be turned on or off by adjusting the flame of the kerosene lamp.

SOUND

Sa-1.   COUPLED PENDULUMS

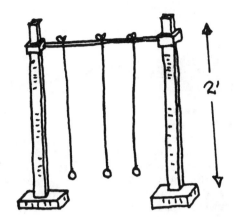

A slightly flexible support is made for three identical simple pendulums.   When one is put into motion with the others initially at rest, the motion is slowly passed from one pendulum to the other in a cyclic manner.

Sa-2.   PROJECTION COUPLED PENDULA

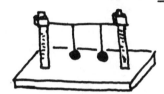

This is the same as Sa-1, except the apparatus is small so it may be placed on an overhead projector. The base is made of clear plastic.

Sa-3.   WAVE PULSE ON A ROPE

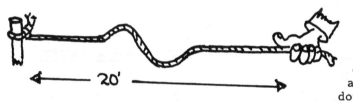

A piece of heavy clothesline is attached to a support and stretched slightly. The other end is given a quick transverse motion, and a pulse is observed traveling down the rope.   The speed of the pulse increases if the rope is pulled more tightly.

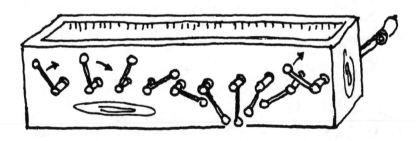

Sa-4.   WATER WAVE MODEL-PHASE VELOCITY

Several horizontal shafts are coupled together by a crankshaft arrangement so they can all be rotated at the same rate.   Rods are connected to each shaft, and can rotate in circles.   Each rod is offset from its neighbor by a fixed phase angle.   As the rods are rotated in one direction, a wave is observed to travel in a particular direction.   If the direction of rotation is reversed, the wave travels in the opposite direction depending on whether the phase angles are leading or lagging.   One can observe the motion of a fixed phase angle.

Sa-5.   STANDING PULSE

A rubber hose loaded with sand is made into a continuous belt and placed over two pulleys which are driven by a variable speed DC motor. The tension of the belt is adjusted so that at some motor speed, the belt moves with the same velocity as a pulse on the belt. The moving belt is struck with a rod, and a standing pulse is observed. In reality, the pulse is moving along the belt in the opposite direction as the belt, but with a speed equal to that of the belt.

Sa-6.   TRAVELING WAVES

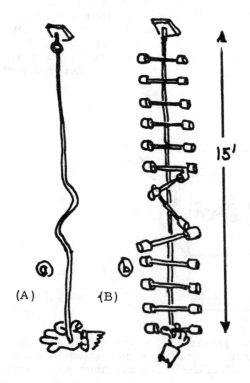

(A)

(B)

(A). A rubber hose filled with sand is suspended from the ceiling. A pulse started at the bottom of the hose travels to the top and is reflected back down the hose. At the bottom there will be a second reflection which is seen to be quite different depending upon whether the bottom end is held or left free.

(B). A set of loaded bars with large moments of inertia is fastened to a thin metal ribbon at regular intervals. The system is hung from the ceiling and a torsion wave is started upward from the bottom. The wave pulse travels quite slowly, allowing details of the reflections to be studied. The reflection at the bottom is different for a fixed or free end. By careful timing, one can obtain standing waves with different numbers of nodes and loops.

Sa-7. WAVE REFLECTIONS AT A DISCONTINUITY

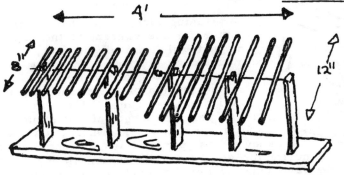

A piece of iron wire (about number 12) has bars attached at regular intervals along it so torsion waves will move on it. If the bars have large moments of inertia and the wire has a weak torsion constant, the waves travel very slowly. Two sets of mounted bars, each giving different phase velocities, may be coupled to form a discontinuity. At the discontinuity there is both transmission and reflection of the waves. A set of bars with graded lengths may be fitted at the coupling to give impedence matches.

PROJECT

Sa-8. TRAVELING AND STANDING WAVES

Two springs are stretched to form rather steeply pitched spirals and mounted so they can turn about a horizontal axis. As the springs are rotated in opposite directions, one observes traveling waves in opposite directions. A third wire, shaped in the form of a sine wave, is placed so the addition of the upper two traveling waves gives nodes and loops is the correct places. The device is observed by projection, allowing the class to see how traveling waves propagating in opposite directions produce the standing wave.

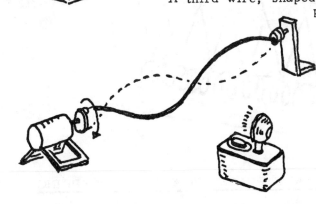

Sa-9. STANDING WAVES

A DC motor is fitted with a small pulley which has a swivel at its periphery for attaching a piece of rope. The other end of the rope is supported by a stand with a swivel. With the rope running loosely over the pulley, the motor is adjusted to run at the speeds which will produce a varying number of nodes and loops on the rope. The motion can be slowed down by viewing the rope with a stroboscope.

Sa-10.   MELDE'S EXPERIMENT

A tuning fork, which has an inter-
rupter for the current to the electromagnet which drives the fork, is
mounted on a board.   A string extends
from one prong of the fork to a pulley
so the tension of the string can be
varied with weights.   The length and
mass per unit length of the string are
known.   From the known tension and
known mass per unit length, one can calculate the velocity of the wave.   One determines
the wave length from the length of the string and
the number of nodes.   The frequency is then calculated
and compared with the value measured with a stroboscope
or that stamped on the tuning fork.

Sa-11.   SPEED OF WAVE GREATER THAN SPEED OF
PARTICLES

A set of sticks is laid in a straight
line with small gaps between them.
The end stick is moved to begin closing the gaps.   The speed at which one observes the gaps closing is much greater than
the speed at which one
moves the sticks.

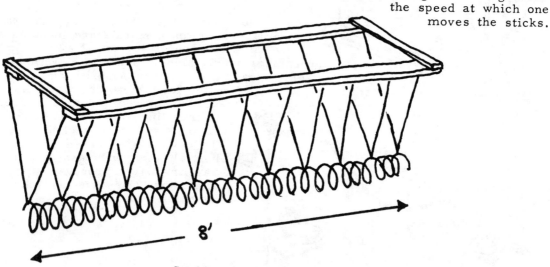

Sa-12.   WAVE PULSES IN A "SLINKY" SPRING

A long "Slinky" spring is suspended horizontally by strings.   Compressional
wave pulses are sent along the spring and the reflections at fixed and free ends
can be studied.

Sa-13. WAVES ON AN AIR TRACK

Any number of identical air track carts are coupled together
with light identical springs.   The transfer of motion from one
cart to the other may be observed in the form of wave pulses.
Reflections of waves from free and bound discontinuities may be
shown.   The system shows the nature of internal energy and
its role in interactions.

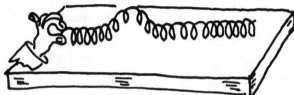

Sa-14. SLINKY
SPRING

A long spring with a
weak spring constant is
layed across the lecture bench.
Wave pulses may be given to the spring which will travel down
the spring.   The properties of reflections from fixed and free
ends may be observed.

Sa-15. CROVA'S DISC

The disc is made by ruling non-concentric circles onto glass
or clear plastic.   The centers of consecutive expanding circles
are moved 1/16 of the distance around a 1/2 inch diameter pilot
circle at the center.   The disc is mounted in an opaque case,
with a viewing slot, so that the disc can rotate about its axis
inside the case.   The view of the disc through the slot may be
projected to show compressions and rarefactions in a sound wave.

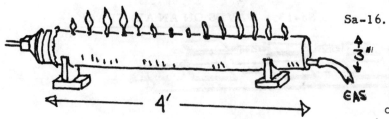

Sa-16.   FLAMING TUBE

A piece of stove pipe has small holes drilled in it at regular intervals of about one inch.   The size of the holes must be adjusted to the gas pressure to produce flames approximately two inches high. One end of the pipe is fitted so illuminating gas can be fed into the pipe, and the other end is fitted with a rubber diaphragm.   When gas passes into the pipe and out the small holes, it may be lighted at each of the holes to give a line of regularly spaced uniform size flames.   A speaker connected to an amplifier and a source of variable frequency is placed next to the rubber diaphragm.   As the frequency is tuned to give standing waves in the pipe, pressure maxima and minima are formed, as indicated by higher and lower flames.

Sa-17.   KUNDT'S TUBE

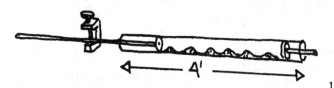

A glass tube is mounted horizontally, and some sawdust is placed along the bottom surface. One end of the tube is fitted with a short piston for tuning the tube length.   The other end is fitted with a metal rod holding a small disc which can close the other end of the tube.   The metal rod is clamped firmly at its center and stroked longitudinally with a chamois skin wetted with alcohol.   The short piston is simultaneously moved until the sawdust forms well defined piles.   The wavelengths of sound in the rod may be compared with the wavelengths of sound in the gas contained in the tube.

Sa-18.   NOISEY KUNDT'S TUBE WITH HOT WIRE

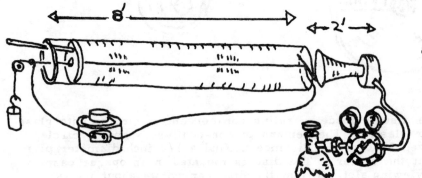

An 8" diameter clear plastic tube has an iron wire stretched down the center.   A piston at one end is used for tuning, and the other end is driven by a horn from a railroad diesel locomotive. The wire is heated to a uniform red heat.   When the horn is turned on, sections of the wire become hotter while others become cooler, indicating the presence of standing waves in the tube.

S-8

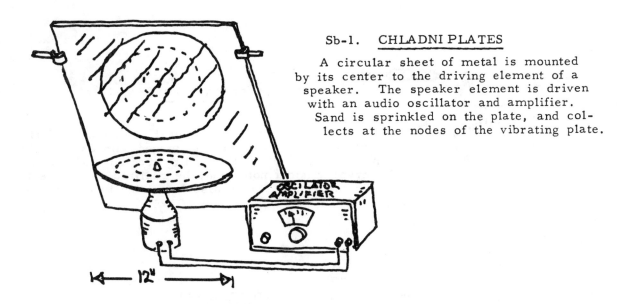

Sb-1. CHLADNI PLATES

A circular sheet of metal is mounted
by its center to the driving element of a
speaker.   The speaker element is driven
with an audio oscillator and amplifier.
Sand is sprinkled on the plate, and collects at the nodes of the vibrating plate.

Sb-2. TWO DIMENSIONAL BIRTHDAY CAKE

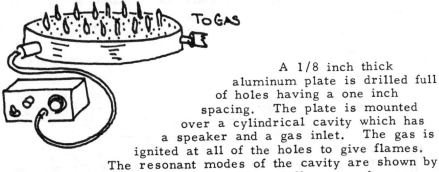

A 1/8 inch thick
aluminum plate is drilled full
of holes having a one inch
spacing. The plate is mounted
over a cylindrical cavity which has
a speaker and a gas inlet.   The gas is
ignited at all of the holes to give flames.
The resonant modes of the cavity are shown by
the relative heights of the flames. Many different modes are
obtained as the frequency is varied.

Sb-3. FORCED NODES AND LOOPS IN A
VIBRATING PLATE

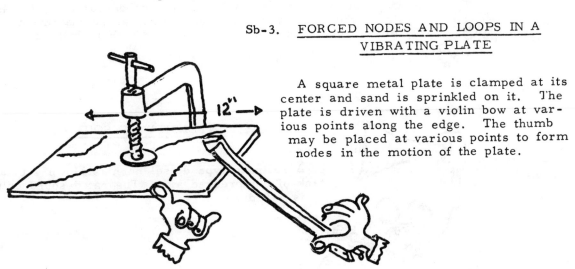

A square metal plate is clamped at its
center and sand is sprinkled on it. The
plate is driven with a violin bow at various points along the edge.   The thumb
may be placed at various points to form
nodes in the motion of the plate.

Sc-1. SIREN DISC

A disc is made with several circles of uniformly spaced holes. The disc is turned with an electric motor, and a jet of air is directed into the holes. Different musical notes may be realized on different circles. The motor speed may also be varied to change the frequency.

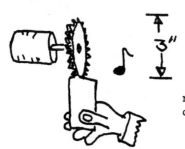

Sc-2. MUSICAL SAW

A dull circular saw blade is mounted on the shaft of a small DC motor. A piece of cardboard held against the teeth of the blade will cause a musical note to be emitted. The pitch of the note changes with the motor speed.

Sc-3. QUADRUPOLE NATURE OF TUNING FORK
SOUND SOURCE

A tuning fork is held close to the ear and rotated about the axis of the handle. Condensations are propagated in opposite directions, while rarefactions are sent in opposite directions at 90° to the condensations. On 45° lines, the interference will give minima, so maxima and minima in intensity are heard as the fork is rotated.

Sc-4. INTENSITY OF SOUND

A railroad type diesel horn is blown with a tank of compressed air. The rated sound output is 110 db.

Sd-1. RESONANCE PENDULA

A set of several pendula are coupled by means of a rotating support. The system is driven by a pendulum consisting of a 1 kilogram brass weight on a rod that is rigidly attached to the rotating support. Only the pendula with the same period as the brass driving pendulum will be in motion. The 180° phase shift across the resonance point is easily observed.

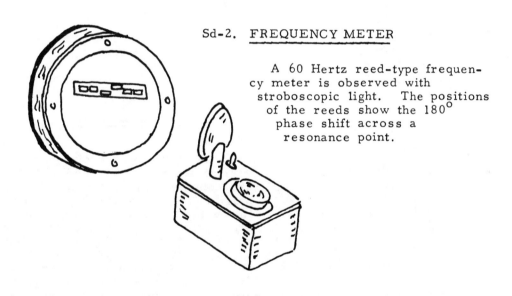

Sd-2. FREQUENCY METER

A 60 Hertz reed-type frequency meter is observed with stroboscopic light. The positions of the reeds show the 180° phase shift across a resonance point.

Sd-3. TUNED RESONANCE BOX

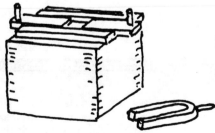

A cubical box has an adjustable hole size. A vibrating tuning fork is held over the hole and the size of the hole is changed. For the proper size hole, a resonance is heard. The adjustment of the hole size changes the mass of air moved in and out of the box.

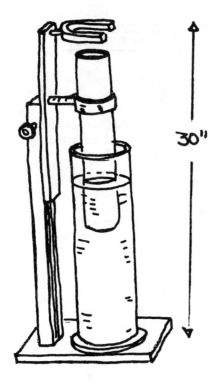

Se-1. RESONANCE TUBE

A tuning fork is mounted above a glass tube, the bottom end of which is closed by the level of water in a tall flask. The tuning fork and top tube are raised and lowered together, giving strong resonances when the length of the air column is an odd multiple of a quarter wavelength of the fork. If the frequency of the fork is known, the velocity of sound may be calculated from this known frequency and the measured wavelength.

Se-2. TUNED BOTTLES

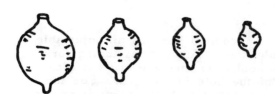

A set of stoppered closed tubes having varying lengths is assembled. The stoppers are actually lengths of tube which fit into the original tubes, causing a lowering of pressure inside the tubes as the stoppers are withdrawn. Each tube selects the frequency corresponding to the quarter wavelength equal to the length of the closed tube from the white noise produced in removing the stopper. A large mailing tube produces a very low bass note when it is pulled apart.

Se-3. HELMHOLTZ RESONATORS

A set of spherical resonators is made of spun brass. Each resonator has one hole for excitation by the sound source, while the second hole fits close to the ear. If the sound has a frequency component close to the characteristic frequency of the resonator, the resonator will go into resonance.

S-12

Se-4. MUSICAL BOTTLES

A set of open bottles may be tuned to various notes of the scale by adding water. The notes are sounded when one blows across the tops.

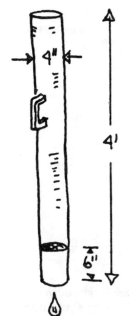

Se-5. HOOT TUBE

A piece of 4 inch diameter stovepipe, approximately 4 feet long, has a screen fastened across the tube about six inches from one end. The source is heated with a Bunsen burner. When the tube is removed from the flame, it produces a loud low pitched "hoot" as the screen cools. If the tube is held sideways the tone stops, but it resumes again when the tube is held vertically.

Se-6. FREQ TUBE

Freq tubes are long open tubes made of corregated plastic and sold as toys. The fundamental or various harmonics of the tube may be excited by holding one end of the tube and swinging it around ones head.

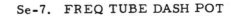

Se-7. FREQ TUBE DASH POT

A freq tube is fastened to a 2 pound coffee can which is open on the bottom. The can is moved up and down in a pail of water to excite the freq tube.

Se-8. MUSICAL GOBLETS

Good quality goblets emit characteristic tones. The goblets can be excited by rubbing around the edge with a wet finger to produce the tones.

S-13

Se-9. ORGAN PIPE

Square organ pipes of several different
lengths are built of spruce. A whistle notch
is made close to one end. The far end has
a plug so the tube may resonate either as a
closed pipe or as an open pipe. The frequency decreases by a factor of two when the
plug is removed.

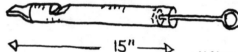

15"

Se-10. VARIABLE PITCH
WHISTLE

A whistle in the form of a tube has a
sliding piston. As the piston is moved in and
out, the tone of the whistle changes.

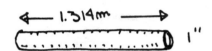

1.314m

1"

Se-11. "C" BAZOOKA

A thin-walled 1 inch brass tube cut to a length of 1.314 meters
will sound a "C" note when blown with the lips as one blows a
horn.

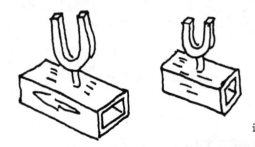

Sf-1. TUNING FORKS WITH
RESONATORS

Several tuning forks corresponding to
notes of the musical scale are mounted on
spruce boxes which are open at each end.
The tone of the fork is much louder than
it is when no resonator is used.

Sf-2. VOWEL TUNING FORKS

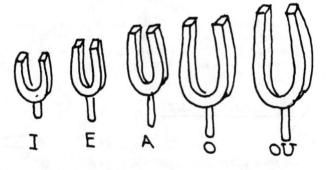

I   E   A   O   OU

A set of special tuning forks has been made that gives
sounds quite similar to those of the spoken vowels.

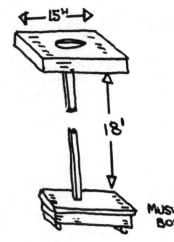

Sf-3. TRANSMISSION OF SOUND THROUGH WOOD

A spruce resonator box is placed on the top of a very long wooden pole that extends through a hole in the floor to a music box at some lower level room. When the music box is started, the tune is heard clearly from the resonator.

Sf-4. ULTRASONIC WAVES

A set of bars made of 3/4" steel rod is suspended by strings. The longest bar has an audible frequency while the shortest is tuned to about 30 kilocycles. As the bars are struck in order, the frequency increases and goes out of the audible range. A microphone and oscilloscope may be used to show that sound is emitted from the short bar.

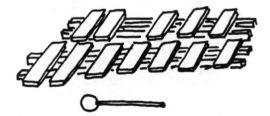

Sf-5. GLOCKENSPIEL

A small xylophone demonstrates the musical scale.

Sf-6. MUSICAL STICKS

A set of musical spruce sticks is cut and sanded until each stick produces a desired note if it is dropped onto a table. The sticks can be tuned to cover the musical scale.

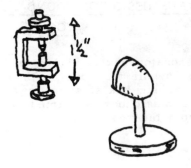

Sg-1. GALTON WHISTLE

A very small whistle with an adjustable gap and adjustable resonant cavity can make sound which varies in frequency from the upper end of the audible range to ultrasonic sound. A microphone and oscilloscope are used to show the presence of ultrasonic waves.

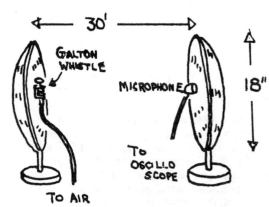

Sg-2. DIRECTIONAL TRANSMISSION OF SHORT WAVELENGTH SOUND

A Galton whistle is placed at the focus of a parabolic mirror. A second parabolic mirror is placed in the directed beam. A microphone that is moved about in the region of the focus of the second mirror will indicate a large amplitude on an oscilloscope when it is at the focal point.

Sg-3. DIFFRACTION OF SOUND

A Galton whistle is placed at the focal point of a parabolic mirror and a small microphone is placed at the focal point of a second parabolic mirror. A set of regularly spaced slats in the form of a picket fence, with spacings considerably less than the wavelength of the sound, is placed between the mirrors. As the receiver microphone and mirror is moved around on the far side of the slats, one finds maxima and minima in the sound intensity at angles which give constructive and destructive interference.

Sg-4. INTERFERENCE OF SOUND

A small speaker is connected to a tube which splits the sound into two parts and subsequently reunites it before the sound emerges from a horn. The lengths of the two paths can be varied by a type of slide trombone arrangement. When the path lengths of the sound are equal or differ by one wavelength, there is a strong sound emitted from the horn. If the path lengths differ by one-half wavelength, the emitted sound is very weak.

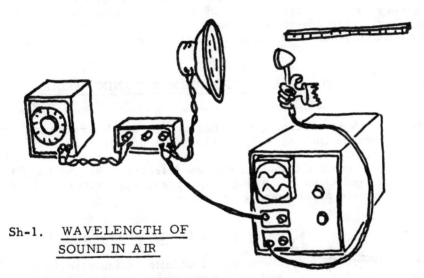

Sh-1. WAVELENGTH OF SOUND IN AIR

An oscillator and amplifier are used to drive a speaker. The input to the speaker is coupled to one input of a dual trace oscilloscope. A microphone in front of the speaker is coupled to the second oscilloscope input, so that two sine waves appear on the face of the oscilloscope. The microphone is then moved away from the speaker until the two sine waves show a phase change corresponding to one wavelength. The distance that the microphone moved is one wavelength. The phase velocity of the wave is the measured wavelength multiplied by the frequency. Several different frequencies can be used to illustrate that the phase velocity is constant.

Sh-2. NO SOUND THROUGH VACUUM

A doorbell is placed under a bell jar which can be pumped down to a reasonable vacuum while the bell is ringing. As the pumping proceeds, the sound vanishes.

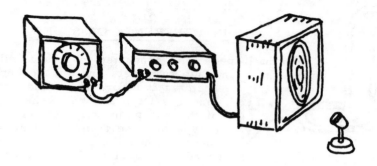

Sh-3. RANGE OF HEARING

An audio oscillator is used to drive an audio amplifier connected to a good speaker. The frequency is varied from 10 to 25000 hertz while the students listen to determine where their cut-off for hearing exists. A microphone and oscilloscope may be used to show that sound is still present.

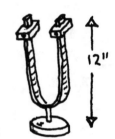

12"

Sh-4. LOW FREQUENCY TUNING FORK

A large tuning fork has an adjustable frequency realized by moving weights along the prongs. If the weights are at the tips, the rate of oscillation is slow and all phases of the motion can be detected. As the weights are moved down the prongs, the frequency increases becoming audible at around 20 hertz.

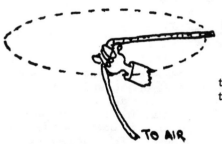

TO AIR

Si-1. DOPPLER SHIFT

A small whistle is inserted into the end of a hose which can be whirled in a horizontal circle. As the whistle is rotated, the frequency becomes higher as it approaches the observer and lower as it moves away from the observer.

Si-2. DOPPLER SHIFT WITH REED

A reed is fastened to an arm which can be rotated by a variable speed motor in a horizontal circle. The listener hears a higher pitch as the reed approaches and a lower pitch as it recedes.

Si-3. DOPPLER SHIFT FROM A TURNTABLE

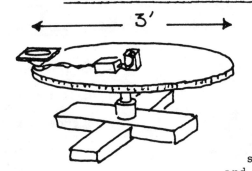

A battery driven 1000 Hz oscillator and amplifier drive a 6 inch upward facing speaker at the periphery of a large turntable. The pitch increases when the speaker approaches the observer and decreases when it recedes from the observer. The direction of rotation can be reversed to show it is not the position of the speaker that changes the tone.

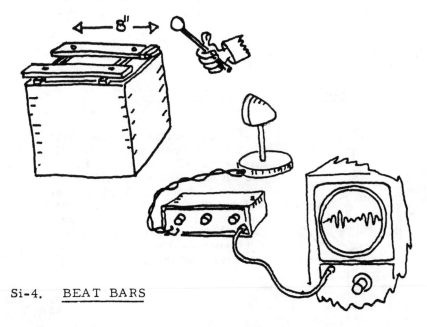

Si-4. BEAT BARS

Two identical bars are mounted on a resonator box, and each is adjusted to give a strong, pure tone as viewed on the oscilloscope. A small additional band, which can be moved along the bar and slightly shift its frequency, is added to one bar. One can hear the beating of the two frequencies when both bars are struck. The beats can be observed with a microphone and oscilloscope. Moving the adjustable band along the bar changes the beating rate.

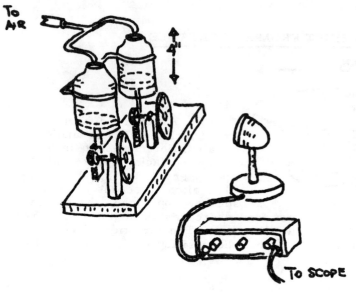

Si-5. BEAT WHISTLES

Two whistles in the form of resonant air bottles with movable pistons can be tuned by adjusting the beat frequency to zero. The effect may be observed with a microphone and oscilloscope. The whistles can be tuned to be as much as one octave apart. As the beat frequency is increased, a rough disonant combination tone develops and eventually becomes a pleasing combination tone when the frequencies have ratios of small whole numbers. One can discuss and listen to all the musical intervals such as:

1n2 - 1n1 = octave	1n6 - 1n5 = minor 3rd
1n3 - 1n2 = 5th	1n8 - 1n5 = minor 6th
1n4 - 1n3 = 4th	1n9 - 1n8 = 2nd
1n5 - 1n4 = major 3rd	1n7 - 1n4 = 7th
1n5 - 1n3 = major 6th	

Si-6. BEATS WITH A LIGHT BEAM

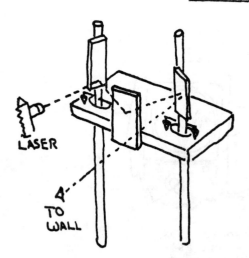

Two physical pendula with slightly different periods oscillate in parallel planes. Each has an attached plane mirror. The stand holds a fixed mirror. A laser beam is reflected from the three mirrors in turn, and projected onto the wall. The light spot shows the beat frequency of the system.

Si-7. CHURCHBELL GUITAR

Swinging a guitar back and forth as it is plucked creates a sound much like that of a church bell.

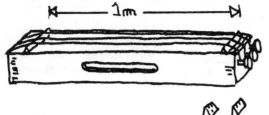

Sj-1.   SONOMETER

A long spruce box is made to carry three tunable strings.
Bridges are placed one meter apart for convenient calculations of string lengths. Some adjustable bridges are made so that the length of each string may be adjusted independently.   The three strings can be tuned to the same pitch by adjusting the beat frequency to zero.

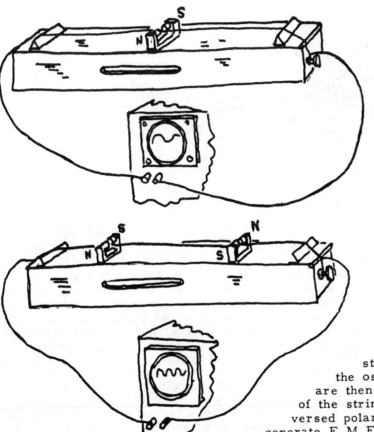

Sj-2.   MODE OF STRING OSCILLATIONS

One can connect the two ends of one of metal strings of the sonometer to an oscilloscope. If an alnico magnet is placed at the center of the string and the string is plucked near the center, an E.M.F. is generated by the changing flux through the magnet. The induced E.M.F. allows the fundamental frequency of the string to be measured with the oscilloscope. Two magnets are then placed one-fourth the length of the string from each end with reversed polarity. The magnets now will generate E.M.F.'s of the fundamental mode that cancel, but the second harmonic has a 180° phase shift as one crosses the node at the center of the string so the E.M.F. of the second harmonic will be relatively large. The frequency measured on the oscilloscope is twice that of the fundamental.

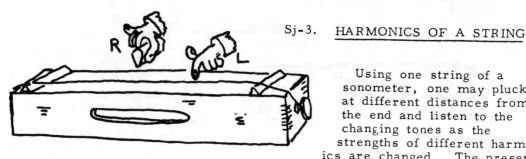

Using one string of a
sonometer, one may pluck
at different distances from
the end and listen to the
changing tones as the
strengths of different harmonics are changed.   The presence
of the harmonics can be detected by
touching a narrow wooden bar at the nodes of various harmonics.   One can
alternately pluck and touch to find strong resonances at several different
octave intervals above the fundamental.

Sj-4.   HARMONIOUS NOTES

Using two strings of the sonometer originally tuned in unison, one places a
bridge under one string so that it is 1/2 the length of the other string.   The
strings then have frequencies one octave apart.   The harmonic test described in
the above experiment is then applied to both strings.   One finds that both strings
have harmonics at the same touch point, but the longer string has twice as
many harmonics as the shorter string up to each nodal touch point.   All
harmonics of the shorter string exist in the longer string.   Next the shorter
string is made 2/3 the length of the longer string to produce an interval of a
5th.   The harmonic test of the previous demonstration now shows that the second harmonic of the short string coincides with the 3rd harmonic of the long
string and the fourth harmonic of the short string coincides with the 6th harmonic of the long string.   One can similarly proceed with all the intervals men-
tioned in Si-5 and find that as one moves to less pleasing intervals the number
of harmonics which coincide will decrease.   A dissonant combination will have
no harmonics in common.

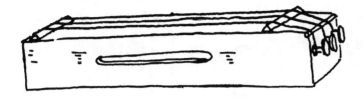

Sj-5. CHORDS

All three strings of the sonometer are used, and are originally tuned in unison. Large acceptable intervals are formed between the first and third strings by placing a bridge under the third string, say at 2/3 the length of the longer string to give an interval of $\ln 3 - \ln 2$. This interval is formed of two smaller acceptable intervals such that

$$\ln 3 - \ln 2 = (\ln 5 - \ln 4) + (\ln 6 - \ln 5).$$

If the second string now has a bridge placed at 4/5 the length of the longer string, the interval between the first and second string is $(\ln 5 - \ln 4)$ and the interval between the second and third strings is $(\ln 6 - \ln 5)$. When the three strings are sounded together, one has a major chord consisting of a major 3rd and a minor 3rd.

One can also write the interval between the first and third strings as

$$\ln 3 - \ln 2 = (\ln 6 - \ln 5) + (\ln 5 - \ln 4).$$

In this case place the bridge under the second string at 5/6 the length of the first string. One now has a minor chord when the three strings are struck together which consists of a minor 3rd and a major 3rd.

Inversions of chords can be found by proceeding in a similar fashion with the intervals;

$$\ln 8 - \ln 5 = (\ln 6 - \ln 5) + (\ln 4 - \ln 3)$$

minor 6th   =   minor 3rd   +   major 4th,

or

$$\ln 8 - \ln 5 = (\ln 4 - \ln 3) + (\ln 6 - \ln 5)$$

minor 6th   =   major 4th   +   minor 3rd.

A second inversion of chords is formed from the interval combination;

$$\ln 5 - \ln 3 = (\ln 4 - \ln 3) + (\ln 5 - \ln 4)$$

major 6th   =   major 4th   +   major 3rd,

$$\ln 5 - \ln 3 = (\ln 5 - \ln 4) + (\ln 4 - \ln 3)$$

major 6th   =   major 3rd   +   major 4th.

Sj-6. ONE STRING VIOLIN

A stick is fastened to a cigar box and a steel string is stretched across the instrument. Tunes may be played.

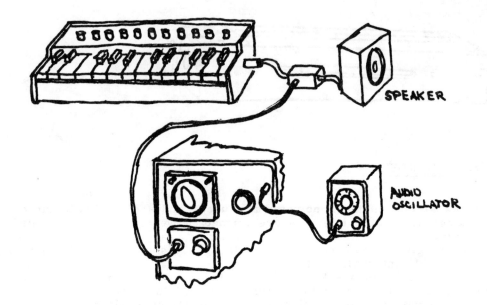

SPEAKER

AUDIO OSCILLATOR

Sk-1.   MUSICAL SCALES

An E. F. Johnson Intonation Trainer is a small electric organ which has
fixed tuning on an even tempered scale.   One can make a tunable scale by
throwing a switch.   On the tunable scale, depress some key such as, say, C
while displaying the tone on the vertical sweep of an oscilloscope.   Tune the
C until it forms a circular Lissajou figure on the oscilloscope with 250 hertz
from an audio oscillator applied to the horizontal sweep.   This horizontal frequency now remains fixed.   Tune the G above C on the organ in the ratio of
3 to 2 by means of a Lissajou figure.   The C and G can be sounded together,
and form a pleasing combination.   This may be compared with the C and G of
an even tempered scale by switching the organ to the even tempered scale.   Next
tune the E above C in the ratio of 5 to 4 by means of a Lissajou figure on the
scope.   Now sound the major chord CEG on this diatonic scale and compare it
with that of the even tempered scale by switching the organ.   One can next tune
E^b with a Lissajou figure having the ratio 6 to 5.   The triad CE^{b}G now gives
a minor triad which may be compared on the diatonic and even tempered scales.
One may construct the entire diatonic scale in this way and compare it with the
even tempered scale.   For details of the complete set of tuning intervals see
Freier, G. D., University Physics.

Sk-2. CIRCULAR GLOCKENSPIEL

A circular glockenspiel is made and tuned to the chromatic
scale.   A sort of tinker toy spool fits over a center post of the
glockenspiel and compresses a spring.   The spool has 12 holes
which can hold mallets.   Major, minor, diminished, and
augmented chords can then be constructed and played chromatically.

Sk-3. ELECTRONIC SYNTHESIZER

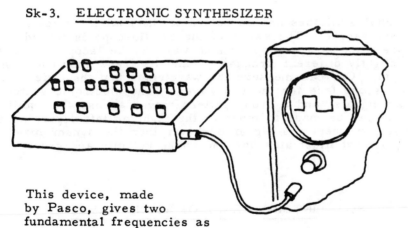

This device, made
by Pasco, gives two
fundamental frequencies as
sine, triangle, or square waves.
The device will generate 9 harmonics of the fundamental which
can be added with varying phase or amplitude.   One can construct
almost any complicated wave form and show the Fourier
components.

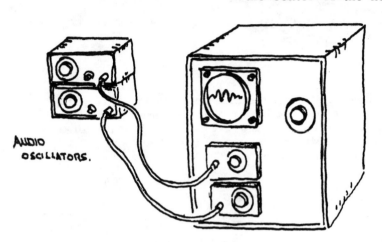

S1-1. BINAURAL HEARING

The relative time of arrival of
sound at our two ears tells us directions of sound sources.   The time
discrimination of our ears can be
measured by holding the two ends of
a long hose to each ear. If someone taps at
the center of the hose, the sound arrives at
both ears simultaneously.
The ears are sufficiently
sensitive to determine
when the tapping is a few
centimeters from the cen-
ter position, correspond-
ing to a time difference
of 10^{-4} seconds.

AUDIO
OSCILLATORS.

S1-2.   PHASE AND GROUP VELOCITY

Two tunable audio oscillators are connected to the dual inputs of an electron-
ically switched oscilloscope. The sweep of the oscilloscope is locked on one of
the inputs, and the trace is a stationary sine wave on the 'scope. The second
oscillator has a slightly different frequency, and its trace shows a slightly
different wavelength. One can measure the wavelength and the difference in
wavelength on the 'scope face for the two waves. The electronic switch is then
set to add the two signals, and a group pattern moves across the oscilloscope
screen. The group can be made to move to the right or left depending on
whether the adjusted frequency is higher or lower than the synchronized frequency. The experiment illustrates how the phase velocity and group velocity
can be different.

S1-3.   INTERFERENCE OF SOUND WAVES

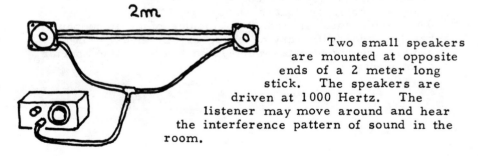

2m

Two small speakers
are mounted at opposite
ends of a 2 meter long
stick.   The speakers are
driven at 1000 Hertz.   The
listener may move around and hear
the interference pattern of sound in the
room.

Sm-1. RIPPLE TANK

A shallow tank with sloping sides is filled with water. Leveling screws allow it to be adjusted so the water depth in the tank can be made uniform. The sloping sides minimize wave reflections. A right angle bar suspended by strings is the driver. A small DC motor is attached to the bar, and drives an eccentric through a train of gears to jostle the bar up and down. The whole vertical face may be placed in the water, or the two balls on wire supports with an adjustable distance between them may be lowered into the water surface.

Sm-2. DOUBLE SOURCE

When the two balls touch the surface, one has two sources in phase. The distance between the balls may be varied.

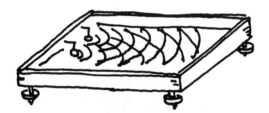

Sm-3. PLANE WAVES

The vertical face of the right angle bar is dipped into the water. The resulting disturbance is caused by an infinite number of sources in phase along a straight line. This develops a plane wave in the water surface. The frequency of the driver is changed to produce different wavelengths.

Sm-4. SINGLE SLIT

Two bars which form a single slit are placed to intercept the plane wave. The wave pattern on the far side of the slit appears the same as that for a single source. The slit width may be increased to form a new line source of oscillators in phase. The wavelength may be changed for various slit openings to show that if the wavelength is short compared to the slit width, the slit produces a geometric shadow.

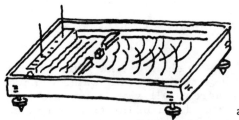

Sm-5.   DOUBLE SLIT

Three bars intercept the plane wave to form a double slit. The wave pattern on the far side appears as that in Sm-2 for a double source. The pattern may be studied as a function of the distance between the slits and the wavelength of the wave.

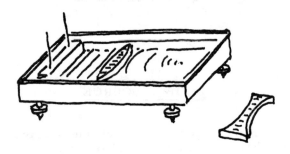

Sm-6.   ACTION OF A LENS

Diverging and converging lenses are made from bars which are less thick than the depth of the water in the tank. When the lens is placed in the tank, the water is quite shallow over the lens. The velocity of the water waves is proportional to the square root of the depth of the water, so that the velocity is low in the shallow region over the lens. As plane waves pass the lens, the center of each wave front is slowed more than the edges for a convex lens. Every plane wave front is changed to a circular wave front which comes to a focus. A diverging lens reverses the curvature given to the plane waves, and makes the wave fronts diverge.

Sn-1.   LISSAJOUS FIGURES IN SAND

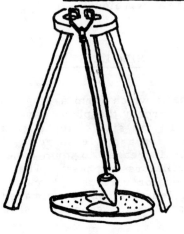

A compound pendulum bob which has two different support points for orthogonal oscillations will trace a Lissajous figure into a pan of sand.

Sn-2.   SAND TRACK LISSAJOUS FIGURES

The compound pendulum has two different support points to give two different lengths to cause oscillations in orthogonal directions. The cone-shaped bob has a hole in the bottom and fine sand is loaded into the bob. Sand leaks from the bob when the pendulum is swinging and traces a Lissajous figure. The relative lengths of the pendulum can be adjusted to give different types of figures.

Sn-3.   LISSAJOUS FIGURES ON AN OSCILLOSCOPE

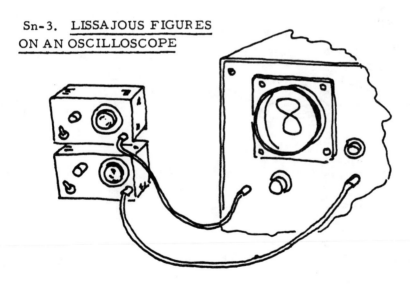

The horizontal and vertical inputs of an oscilloscope are driven by two different audio frequency generators. Any desired Lissajous figure may be obtained.

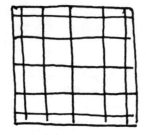

Sn-4. LISSAJOUS COORDINATE
SYSTEM

A coordinate system consisting
of lines whose distances from an
axis are proportional to the sines of
0°, 30°, 60°, and 90° is sketched
onto the blackboard. One can start
anywhere on the coordinate system and draw any desired
rational frequency ratio. Locate points on the graph by moving
n increments horizontally and m increments vertically, always
turning back into the diagram when the edge is reached. The
importance of the phase angle can be shown easily. The value
of the phase angle is determined by the starting point on the
diagram. For more details see, G. Freier, University Physics,
Experiment and Theory, Appleton-Century-Crofts, New York,
1965. pp 144-145.

So-1. METRONOME

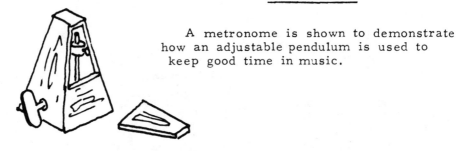

A metronome is shown to demonstrate
how an adjustable pendulum is used to
keep good time in music.

OPTICS

POINT SOURCE

DIFFUSE SOURCE

Oa-1. STRAIGHT LINE PROPAGATION OF LIGHT

A commercial point source is used to project shadows of apparatus. There is a neglible penumbra, so that many experiments may be done in projection. For contrast the same objects may be projected by an ordinary light bulb. One can make a very good point source from some of the small auto lamps or pilot light lamps which have tightly wound filaments.

←—5"—→

Oa-2. PINHOLE PROJECTION

A light bulb with a long filament is placed in a can and sealed on the end with a piece of paper. While the bulb is pointed at the wall, pinholes are pricked into the paper. As each hole is produced, a new image of the filament appears on the wall. After several images are formed, it is interesting to see them all brought together into one bright image with a converging lens.

Oa-3. PINHOLE CAMERA

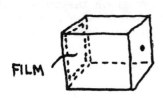

FILM

A black box with a pinhole opening is made. A piece of cut film is taped in the back. Some pictures of scenery may be taken ahead of time with different size holes to show the effect of hole size.

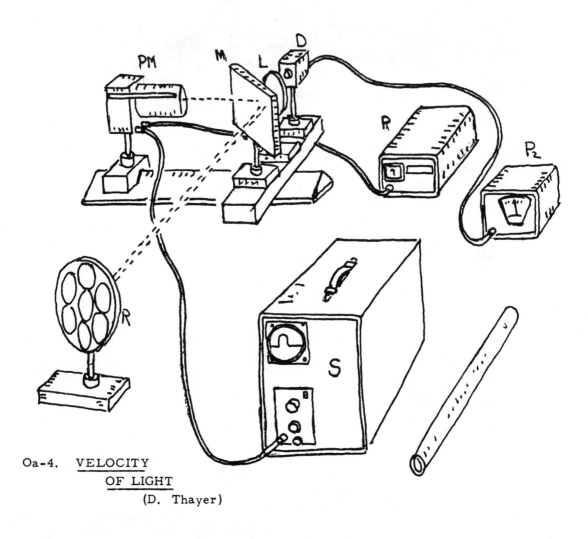

Oa-4. VELOCITY
OF LIGHT
(D. Thayer)

The experiment is used to determine the group velocity of light by measuring the time interval necessary for light to travel a known distance. This distance can be as small as one meter. The light emitting diode, D, sends out pulses with a repetition rate of 22 kilohertz. Energy to the diode is furnished by the 200 volt power supply P_2. The light pulse travels through the lens L, through the plate glass M to the bicycle reflectors R, and then back to the plate glass which now acts as a mirror and directs the light into a 1P22 photomultiplier operated at 1500 volts from the power supply P_1. The oscilloscope is triggered by the transmitted pulse, so the return pulse is displayed on the screen. As the reflector is moved, the pulse changes position on the scope face. The velocity of light is then found by finding how much this pulse moves on the time scale while the reflector is moved a known distance. A one meter tube is provided which can be filled with other fluids, allowing one to measure the slower group velocities in these media. (See AJP, 41, p722)

Ob-1. REFLECTION FROM SMOOTH AND ROUGH SURFACES

A bright lamp such as a carbon arc forms a parallel beam
which is reflected from a plane
mirror and gives a clear cut spot
on a screen. Chalk dust is then
sprinkled onto the mirror and the image on
the screen becomes blurred.

Ob-2. POSITION OF IMAGE

A piece of plate glass is mounted vertically
in a darkened room. A candle is placed in
front of the glass, and a glass of water is placed
an equal distance behind the glass. The candle
image appears in the glass of water for all observers.

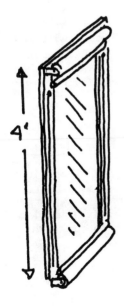

Ob-3. HEIGHT OF MIRROR FOR FULL VIEW

A dressing mirror with window shades at the top
and bottom is mounted vertically. As a person stands
in front of the mirror, he adjusts the shades until he
can just see his entire height. The distance between
the shades will be half of the person's height. The
measurement is independent of how far the person
stands from the mirror.

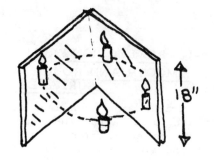

Ob-4.   MIRRORS AT AN ANGLE

Two mirrors are hinged together and placed on the table. A candle placed between them produces any number of images all on a circle. The number of images depends on the angle between the mirrors.

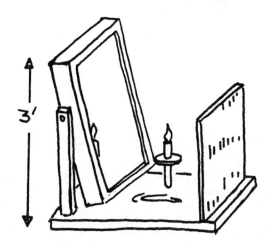

Ob-5.   PARALLEL MIRRORS

This is a variation of the above experiment, but allows one to have a zero degree angle between the mirrors. At zero degrees, one gets an infinite number of images on a straight line.

Ob-6.   STRAIGHT BACK REFLECTOR

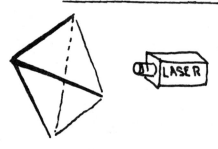

Reflectors are placed together to form surfaces like the inside corner of a box. A laser beam directed into the reflector will always come straight back.

Ob-7.   INVERTED IMAGE

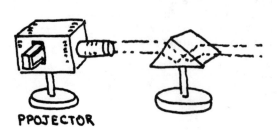

A slide is placed into a projector to form an inverted image. A large right angle prism is placed in the beam to make the image erect.

Ob-8. OPTICAL DISC

    This is a ground glass rotatable disc, which makes the rays of light more observable. Various lenses or mirrors are placed at the center of the disc, while illuminated with parallel light rays entering through slits at one edge. If ground glass is not available, the rays can be made quite visible with chalk dust. One can show that the angle of incidence equals the angle of reflection for a plane mirror.

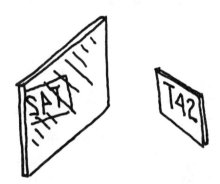

Ob-9. PERVERSION

    The image of an automobile license plate is studied in a plane mirror. One gets perversion, but no inversion.

Ob-10. ELLIPTICAL TANK

    An elliptical shaped wall is made of shiny aluminum. A line filament lamp is placed at one focus. When chalk dust or smoke is sprayed into the tank, a bright image appears at the other focus.

Ob-11. BLACKBOARD OPTICS - PLANE
MIRROR

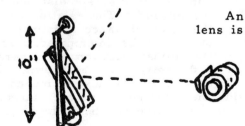

    An enclosed light source with a cylindrical lens is stuck to the blackboard by a suction cup. The light source produces a pencil of light which is parallel to the blackboard surface. A plane mirror surface is also held to the blackboard by suction cups, and reflects the beam so that the angle of incidence equals the angle of reflection.

Oc-1. BLACKBOARD OPTICS - CONCAVE MIRROR

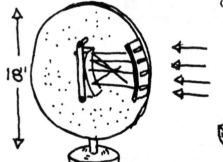

A concave mirror is held in the holder described above. The source is then
rotated and the reflected beam will always
pass through the focal point of the system,
which is located on the optical axis and
halfway between the mirror surface and the
center of curvature.

Oc-2. BLACKBOARD OPTICS-CONVEX
MIRROR

A convex mirror is held in the holder
described above. The source is rotated, and
the reflected beam always appears to emanate
from the focal point of the mirror. The focal point
is located on the optical axis and halfway between the
mirror surface and the center of curvature.

Oc-3. OPTICAL DISC - CURVED MIRRORS

Both concave and convex mirrors may be
mounted in the optical disc described in
Ob-8. Several rays are transmitted at once
and clearly define the focal points of the two
types of mirrors.

Oc-4. IMAGE WITH A CONCAVE MIRROR

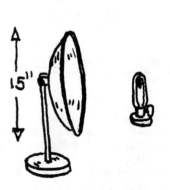

A long filament light bulb is
placed in front of a concave mirror at a distance from the mirror
greater than the focal point. An
image is formed on a screen at
some other discrete distance from
the mirror. The relation between
the object distance and image distance may be determined. The
linear magnification and inversion
of the image may be shown. The
light source may next be moved inside the focal point and one can show
that no real image can be formed.

Oc-5. AMUSEMENT PARK MIRRORS

Convex and concave cylindrical mirrors with a radius of curvature of 10 inches are made of chrome plated sheet metal and mounted on stands. Images will be erect in one mirror and inverted in the other.

Oc-6. RED BALL IN MIRROR

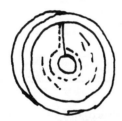

A red ball is suspended as a pendulum at the center of curvature of a well silvered hemispherical concave mirror. Both the motion of the object and the image can be observed as the red ball pendulum swings.

Oc-7. FIND THE OBJECT

Two well silvered concave mirrors are made. The top mirror has a 1.5 inch unsilvered hole so that light can escape. A ring is placed at the bottom of the bottom mirror. When the top mirror rests on the bottom mirror, the final image rests on the surface of the clear hole. The mirrors must have the correct curvature and separation to get the final image in the desired location.

Oc-8. NO IMAGE WITH A CONVEX MIRROR

A lamp is placed in front of a convex mirror and no image point can be found. The class can look into the mirror and see the wide angle image.

Oc-9. LIGHTING A CIGARETTE

An arc lamp is directed into a parabolic mirror over a long distance. A cigarette may be lighted at the focal point of the mirror.

Oc-10. IMAGE OF FLOWER IN A VASE

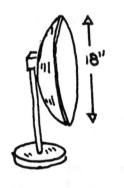
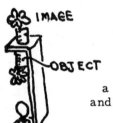

A stand which holds an inverted flower and flower vase is built so that it and the illumination for it are hidden behind a vertical board. When the stand is placed in front and at the center of curvature of a concave mirror, an image of the flower and vase appears on the top of the stand.

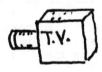

Oc-11. COLD CANDLE

A lighted candle is placed at the center of curvature of a concave mirror, but slightly off the axis so the inverted image can be formed to one side. The object and image are viewed with a TV camera focused on both the object and image. One may hold his finger in the image candle flame.

Od-1. REFRACTION AT THE SURFACE OF WATER

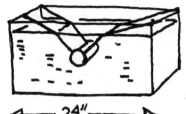

A glass tank is filled with water dyed with fluorescein. A submerged light source which can form pencils of light is in the tank. As the pencils of light leave the water surface, they are bent away from the normal to the surface.

Od-2. BLACKBOARD OPTICS-REFRACTION

A light source with a cylindrical lens is stuck to the blackboard by means of a suction cup. The source emits a beam of light that travels parallel to the blackboard. Similar suction cup holders hold a parallel sided piece of 3/4 thick clear plastic in the beam. The beam emerges parallel to the original beam, showing that the bending of the beam toward the normal on entering and away from the normal on emerging is the same. A prism shaped piece of plastic may be inserted to show how the direction of a light beam may be changed.

Od-3. LAW OF REFRACTION

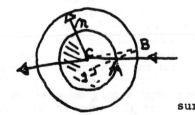

A optical disc holds a semicircular slab of glass. If a single ray is used and allowed to strike the center of curvature of the slab, there will be refraction only at the entrance of the ray into the slab and no refraction when the ray emerges. The angles may be measured to verify that the sine of the angle of incidence divided by the sine of the angle of refraction always gives a constant value equal to the index of refraction. One can rule on the surface of the disc two circles which have the ratio n:1. Suppose the incident ray cuts the unit circle at A. A perpendicular is dropped to the refracting surface and extended back to B on the circle of radius n. A line from B to the point C where the light strikes the refracting surface gives the direction of the refracted ray.

Od-4. SEEING A COIN

A coin is placed into the bottom of a container and a television camera is aimed over the edge. The coin can not be seen when the container is empty, but it can be seen when the container is filled with water. The light rays from the coin are refracted at the water surface and enter the television camera.

Od-5. BROKEN STICK

A stick placed in water appears to be broken at the surface.

Od-6. APPARENT DEPTH

A tall flask is filled with water and a coin is placed at the bottom. An observer looks in from the top and estimates the depth of the coin. The index of refraction of the water is then calculated as the real depth divided by the apparent depth.

Od-7. INDEX OF REFRACTION BY APPARENT DEPTH

A TV camera is mounted so that it can move vertically measured distances. The camera is first focused on a spot on the table. A 6 inch piece of clear plastic is then placed over the spot and the camera is moved until the same spot is again in focus. The distance that the camera was moved is noted. One now has information on the real thickness of the block (which may be checked by a direct measurement) and the apparent thickness so that the index of refraction of the plastic may be calculated.

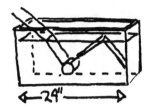

Oe-1. CRITICAL ANGLE

A rectangular tank filled with water containing fluorescein dye has a submerged light source which produces pencils of light. The source is rotated until the angle of refraction is 90°. Further rotation of the source gives total reflection at the surface.

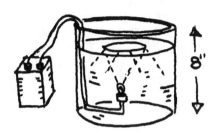

Oe-2. LIGHT BELOW SURFACE

A small light is sealed so that it may operate under water and placed in a jar of water. For better visibility, a powder is sprinkled on the surface. Only a central spot of light is visible, and the size of the light cone is determined by the critical angle.

Oe-3. BLACK BALL TURNS SILVER

A glass bulb thoroughly blackened with camphor soot is submerged in a flask of water. The air trapped in the soot caused light to be reflected from the soot surface at the critical angle. As a result, the ball will appear silver over much of its surface.

Oe-5. TOTAL REFLECTION FROM WATER SURFACE

Some benzol is floated on water in a beaker. A light beam entering the side of the beaker into the benzol will be totally reflected at the water surface.

Oe-4. MERCURY IN A TEST TUBE

A test tube is partially filled with mercury and submerged in a beaker of water. When it is viewed from above, one cannot discern the location of the mercury level in the test tube.

Oe-6. LIGHT SCATTERING FROM ICE

A beam of light is made to pass through a parallel sided glass container filled with cold chipped ice or cold snow. The beam is scattered mostly at the critical angle as it emerges from the ice crystals, and gives the snow or ice its white or silver color. Water is then added to the snow and changes the critical angle so the beam of light penetrates the sample which loses its white or silver color.

Oe-7. LIGHT PIPE

A spiral is made of clear plastic rod and mounted in a base which conceals a light bulb. Light enters the end of the rod and travels around the spiral by reflection from the sides at the critical angle, eventually emerging at the other end of the spiral.

Of-1. MINIMUM DEVIATION OF A PRISM

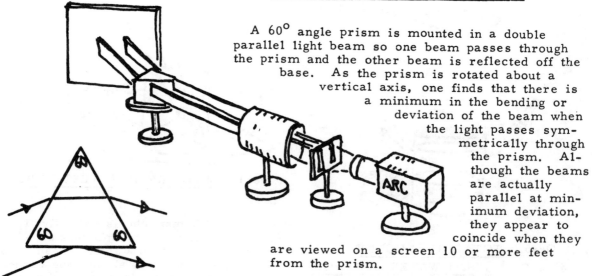

A $60°$ angle prism is mounted in a double parallel light beam so one beam passes through the prism and the other beam is reflected off the base. As the prism is rotated about a vertical axis, one finds that there is a minimum in the bending or deviation of the beam when the light passes symmetrically through the prism. Although the beams are actually parallel at minimum deviation, they appear to coincide when they are viewed on a screen 10 or more feet from the prism.

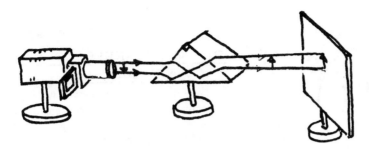

Of-2.   INVERSION OF IMAGE

Slides are placed in a projector so they are projected upside down.   A
large 90° prism is placed in the beam so there is total reflection from the hypotenuse face.   The image is then erect.

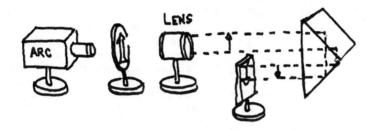

Of-3.   DOUBLE REFLECTION AT THE CRITICAL ANGLE

Light enters the hypotenuse face of a 90° prism and makes a reflection at
each of the leg faces.   The beam is reversed in direction, and the image is
inverted by the prism.

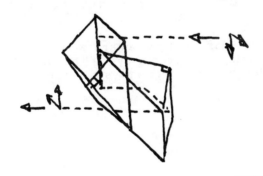

Of-4.   DOUBLE REFLECTION IN TWO DIMENSIONS

If two 90° prisms are arranged as shown, the image is inverted by one
prism and perverted by the other.

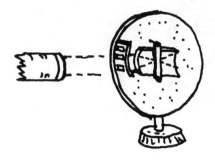

Og-1. OPTICAL DISC-REFRACTION AT CURVED SURFACES

A long plastic slab with a convex surface and a concave surface is mounted on the optical disc. The refraction toward and away from the normal can be traced.

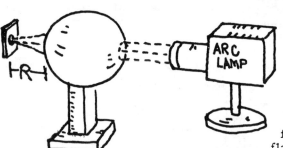

Og-2. WATER LENS

A parallel beam of light enters one side of a flask filled with water. An image is formed at a distance equal to the radius of the flask from the far surface of the flask. Fluorescein dye may be placed in the water to help trace the rays through the flask.

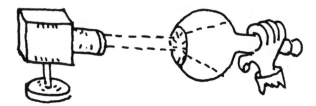

Og-3. DIVERGING BEAM

A parallel beam of light enters a flask filled with water containing fluorescein dye. The flask has a "wine bottle" bottom so the rays diverge.

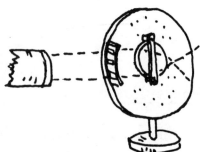

Og-4. OPTICAL DISC-CIRCULAR GLASS PLATE

A circular slab of glass is mounted on the optical disc, as an example of a thick lens. The distance of the image from the surface may be shown to be different for glass than for water as found in Og-2.

Og-5. THIN CONVEX LENS

A light bulb serves as an object for a convex lens. The relation between the object and image distance may be shown. One also shows that the image is real, inverted, and has a linear magnification of the image distance divided by the object distance, as long as the object distance is greater than the focal length. One can also show that when the object distance is less than the focal length, there is no real image.

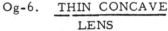

Og-6. THIN CONCAVE LENS

With the same arrangement as described in Og-5, one shows that no real image can be found with a diverging lens.

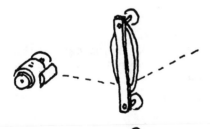
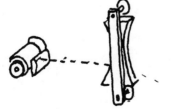

Og-7. BLACKBOARD OPTICS-THIN LENSES

The light source described in Od-2 is mounted in front of models of thin lenses. As the light source in front of the convex lens is rotated, the light beam always passes through a point on the far side of the lens called the image point. For the concave lens, this point is on the front side of the lens, and the ray only appears to emerge from this point. This is a virtual image.

Og-8.   MODEL OF·THE EYE

A model of the eye
may be taken apart to
show its optical elements.

Og-9.   LIGHT RAYS THROUGH LENSES

    Two lasers form rays whose paths are visible by light
scattered from chalk dust. Various lenses may be placed in the
rays to show the action of the lenses. The geometry of various
types of optical instruments may be shown.

Og-10. OPTICAL DISC-LENSES

Lens sections with different radii of curvature are mounted on the optical disc, and their focal points may be shown. One can demonstrate the relations between focal length, radius of curvature, and index of refraction by using lenses of different radii and different indicies of refraction. By including air lenses, one may show the effects of ordering the surfaces with respect to the changing index of refraction; i.e. a convex air lens is diverging.

Og-11. WATCH GLASS LENS

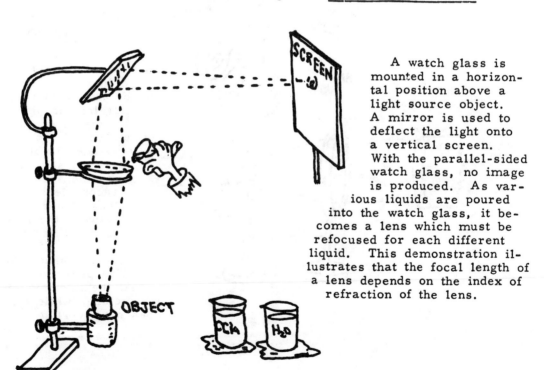

A watch glass is mounted in a horizontal position above a light source object. A mirror is used to deflect the light onto a vertical screen. With the parallel-sided watch glass, no image is produced. As various liquids are poured into the watch glass, it becomes a lens which must be refocused for each different liquid. This demonstration illustrates that the focal length of a lens depends on the index of refraction of the lens.

Og-12.   FOCAL LENGTH
OF A LENS

A lamp is placed in front of a converging lens as an object.   A plane mirror directly behind the lens reflects the light back onto a ground glass screen to give an image.   When the screen and lamp are at the same distance from the lens, the distance to the lens is the focal length of the lens.

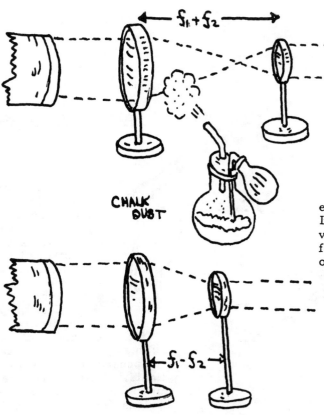

CHALK DUST

$f_1 + f_2$

$f_1 - f_2$

Og-13.   CHANGING BEAM
SIZE WITHOUT INVERSION

A parallel light beam is directed into a converging lens. In the first part, a second converging lens is placed behind the first a distance equal to the sum of the focal lengths.   Chalk dust or smoke is blown into the beam to show its presence. For the second case, the second lens is a diverging lens placed so the distance between the lenses is equal to the difference of the focal lengths.   If the original beam is made that from a slide projector, one can show that the first system will invert the picture, while the second one does not invert it.

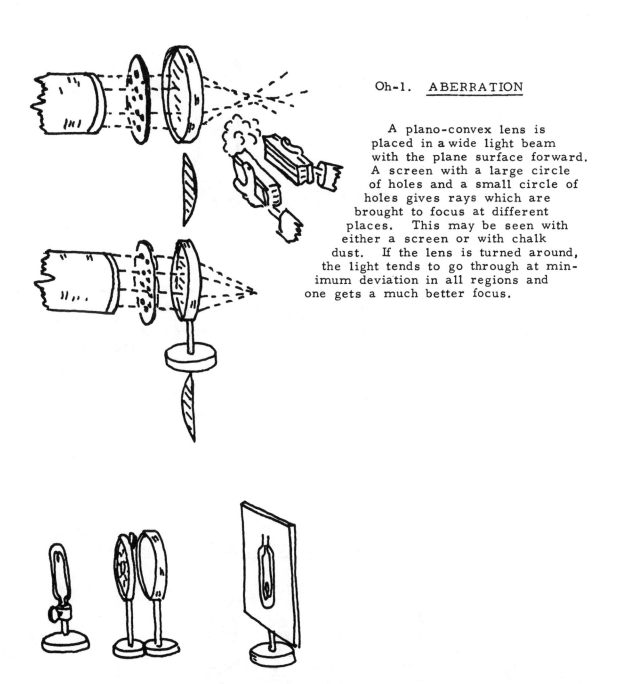

Oh-1. <u>ABERRATION</u>

A plano-convex lens is placed in a wide light beam with the plane surface forward. A screen with a large circle of holes and a small circle of holes gives rays which are brought to focus at different places. This may be seen with either a screen or with chalk dust. If the lens is turned around, the light tends to go through at minimum deviation in all regions and one gets a much better focus.

Oh-2. <u>IMPROVING AN IMAGE WITH A STOP</u>

A relatively short focal length lens is used to form an image of a lamp. An iris diaphragm stop is placed in front of the lens and shows that a small opening will greatly improve the sharpness of the image, but it cuts down the intensity.

Oh-3. DEPTH OF FOCUS

A six inch coil of nichrome wire, which is heated and held in a horizontal
position approximately along the axis of a converging lens, serves as an extended object. An iris diaphragm is placed in front of the lens. With the hole
in the diaphragm as small as possible, the whole length of the object is in
focus at once. But if the stop is wide open, only a small section is in focus
at one time. The f number for the stop may be defined as the ratio of the focal
length to the diameter of the stop. One has a large depth of focus with a large
f number. If the object and image are moved to new positions so the linear
magnification, say, increases, one can demonstrate that the length of the object
that is in focus is inversely proportional to the square of the linear magnification.

Oh-4. USE OF CROSS HAIRS AND SUPERPOSITION OF IMAGES

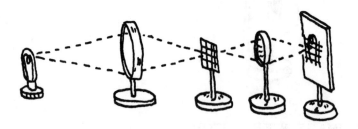

A real image is formed with a converging lens. A wire screen is placed at
this image point. A second converging lens forms an image of the first image
point on the screen. One sees the image of the lamp and the wire screen
superposed. One may replace the wire screen with a slide of some picture.

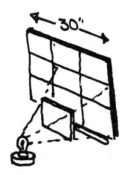

Oi-1. INVERSE SQUARE LAW

A rectangular paddle and a
screen with 9 zones, each the area
of the paddle, are constructed. A
point source of light projects
shadows onto the screen. The
relation between intensity, area,
and distance is demonstrated.

Oi-2. RUMFORD
PHOTOMETER

Shadows of an opaque object
are adjusted until the illumination per unit area is the same
for each shadow. The source
strengths of the sources may now be compared by equating illuminations per unit area,
which properly corrects for the inverse square
law.

Oi-3. GREASE SPOT PHOTOMETER

A piece of paper with a spot of grease on it is placed between two lamps.
When the contrast of the greased spot to the ungreased paper is a minimum,
one can equate the illumination per unit area for the two sources. The action
of the grease spot is such that, at balance, the light transmitted by one lamp
is replaced by the transmission from the other lamp. This is equivalent to
all light being reflected from the spot. The assumption above requires that the
reflecting paper be good white paper, and that there is no absorbtion in the
grease spot.

Oi-4.   PARAFFIN BLOCK PHOTOMETER

Two blocks of paraffin are cemented together while separated by a shiny aluminum sheet. One adjusts the position of the block until both sides appear to be equally bright. The amount of scattered light is then the same for the two blocks. Since the areas are the same on both sides, the illumination per unit area will be the same at balance.

Oi-5. RADIATION LAWS

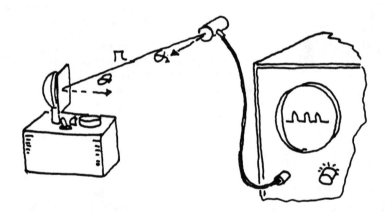

A translucent sheet is placed over a stroboscope. A photodetector such as a phototransistor covered with a translucent sheet is connected to an oscilloscope. The amplitude of the signal for changes in the angles θ_1 , θ_2 , or the distance, r , may be shown.

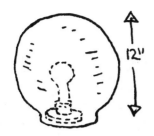

Oi-6. SURFACE BRIGHTNESS

A lamp with a designated candlepower may be considered as a point source. When the lamp is enclosed
with a frosted bulb, one can reduce the candlepower
to surface brightness per unit area.

Oi-7. SURFACE BRIGHTNESS OF A
REFLECTING SURFACE

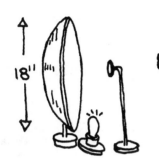

A bright orange piece of paper is illuminated
and placed at an object point of a large concave
mirror. If the eye is at the image point, the entire surface of the large mirror appears to have
the same brightness as the orange piece of paper,
even though the illumination from the spot is spread
over a much greater area.

Oi-8. SURFACE BRIGHTNESS OF
A LENS

A light is made sufficiently dim with
a variac so that one can look at it with
the eye quite close to the lamp. One
places the eye at the image point of a lens
focused on the light, and the entire lens has
the surface brightness of the source. Do not
do this with a bright light or the sun.

Oi-9. INTEGRATION OF LIGHT PULSES BY THE EYE

Increase the frequency of light pulses from a strobotac
until the light appears to be continuous. This will be at
approximately 3000 cycles per minute. The intensity is
then cut about in half by a filter or partially crossed
polaroids, and the light appears to be continuous
at a frequency as low as 1700 cycles per minute. For greater extinction of the light source,
the frequency at which the light appears to be
continuous will be still lower.

FILTER

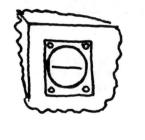

Oi-10. JARRING THE EYEBALL

If one observes a free running oscillo-scope which has a straight-line trace and stomps his foot, a false pulse appears on the trace of the oscilloscope. The sweep frequency should be adjusted to get the best shaped pulse.

Oi-11. EYE MOST SENSITIVE TO GREEN LIGHT

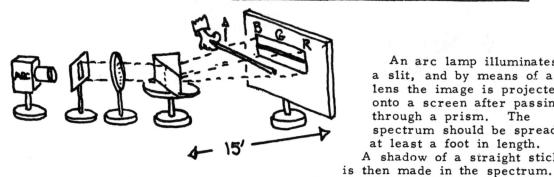

An arc lamp illuminates a slit, and by means of a lens the image is projected onto a screen after passing through a prism. The spectrum should be spread at least a foot in length.

A shadow of a straight stick is then made in the spectrum.

As the shadow is moved up or down, it appears to bend with the leading edge in the green part of the spectrum. The eye responds more rapidly to the green light.

Oi-12. RETINAL FATIGUE

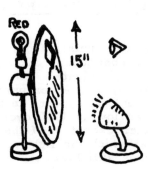

A red light is mounted behind an opening in a disc which can be rotated in either direction. Half of the disc is white and half of the face of the disc is black. The viewing side of the disc is illuminated with white light. If the disc is rotated so that one sees the red bulb followed by a black section of the disc, the light appears to be red. If the direction of rotation is reversed so that one sees the red light followed by white, the bulb appears to be green. In this latter case, the red receptors are fatigued by the flash of red light and when viewing the white surface, one sees the com-plementary color green.

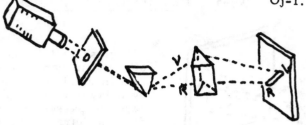

Oj-1.   PURITY OF THE SPECTRUM

A beam of parallel light passes through a hole in a screen and is broken into colors to form a spectrum along a vertical line. A second prism mounted vertically intercepts the spectrum and bends each color separately without breaking the colors down into further colors.

Oj-2.   SYNTHESIS OF COLORS

A disc is colored in sectors with the colors of the spectrum.   When the disc is rotated, it appears to be white.

Oj-3.   COLOR BOX

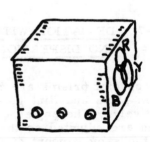

A system is built which can project varying amounts of red, yellow, or blue light onto a transluscent screen.   One can construct various colors in the overlapping areas of the projected colors by varying the intensity of each primary color.

Oj-4.   RECOMBINING THE SPECTRUM

A spectrum is produced in the usual way with a prism. A converging lens placed in the spectrum will bring it together to form white light. If a section of the spectrum is removed, one gets the complimentary color on the screen.

Oj-5.   DISPERSION OF LIQUIDS

A glass cell in the shape
of a prism has a layer of
carbon disulfide covered
by a layer of water.
Light is passed through to
form spectra in the usual
way.   Carbon disulfide,
because of its greater dispersion, produces a spectrum
that is much more spread out
than that produced by the water.

Oj-6.   DISPERSION IN DIFFERENT MEDIA

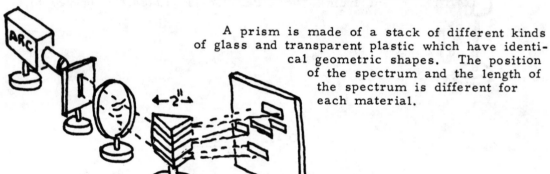

A prism is made of a stack of different kinds
of glass and transparent plastic which have identical geometric shapes.   The position
of the spectrum and the length of
the spectrum is different for
each material.

Oj-7.   DEVIATION WITH
NO DISPERSION

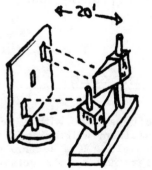

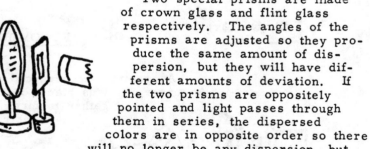

Two special prisms are made
of crown glass and flint glass
respectively.   The angles of the
prisms are adjusted so they produce the same amount of dispersion, but they will have different amounts of deviation.   If
the two prisms are oppositely
pointed and light passes through
them in series, the dispersed
colors are in opposite order so there
will no longer be any dispersion, but
there will be a net deviation.

Oj-8. DISPERSION WITH NO DEVIATION

Two special prisms are made of crown glass and flint glass respectively. The angles of the prisms are adjusted so that they give the same deviation, but give different amounts of dispersion. If the two prisms point in opposition, and are used in series, there will be no net deviation, but there will still be dispersion.

Oj-9. CHROMATIC ABERRATION IN A LENS

Light from an arc source is directed by a large converging lens with a short focal length through a screen having a circle of holes that allow light to pass only through the outer edge of the lens. Sections of the lens behind each hole will then act as prisms which have dispersion. The net effect is that the lens has a shorter focal length for blue light than for red light. If an iris diaphragm is placed beyond the red focal point, it can be opened so that only red light gets to the screen. If the diaphragm is moved ahead of the blue focal point, it can screen out the red light and allow only blue light to reach the screen.

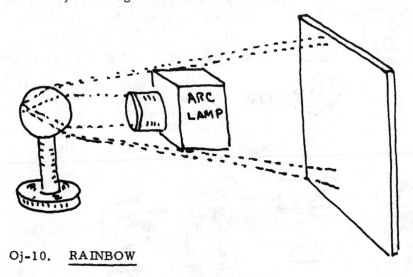

Oj-10. RAINBOW

A large arc lamp projector is directed at a 4 inch sphere filled with water. The screen in back of the projector is illuminated with a circular rainbow.

O-29

Ok-1. ULTRAVIOLET SPECTRUM

An open carbon arc (no glass lens) is focused with a quartz lens through a quartz prism to a screen. The top part of the screen is white paper and the bottom part is fluorescent paper. The spectrum appears to be much longer at the ultraviolet end on the fluorescent paper than on the white paper.

Ok-2. BLACK LIGHT

An ultraviolet "black light" lamp is used to illuminate fluorescent materials such as rocks, oil, teeth, starched shirts and fluorescent light bulbs. These substances absorb ultraviolet light and reradiate in the visible portion of the spectrum.

Ok-3. PHOTOELECTRIC EFFECT

A piece of freshly polished zinc is placed on an electroscope and illuminated with an open carbon arc lamp (no glass lens). The beam is brought to a focus on the zinc by means of a quartz lens. A positively charged electroscope will not discharge when the light shines on the zinc plate. A negatively charged electroscope will quickly lose its charge, showing that negative charges (electrons!) are ejected from the zinc surface by the light. If a piece of glass is held in the beam, the discharge process stops because the visible part of the spectrum is not responsible for the ejection of the electrons. The glass acts as a filter for the ultraviolet light.

Ok-4. PHOTOELECTRIC EFFECT PRODUCED WITH ULTRAVIOLET LIGHT

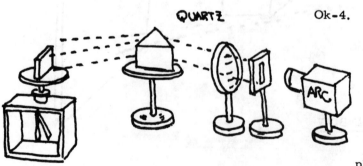

The experiment described in Ok-3 is redone with the addition of a quartz prism and a slit, allowing the zinc plate to be exposed to various sections of the spectrum. The discharge of the negatively charged electroscope is realized when the portion of the spectrum beyond the violet end strikes the zinc plate.

O1-1. WAVE NATURE OF ELECTROMAGNETIC RADIATION

A 12 cm wave-length radar oscil-lator is connected to a small dipole antenna. A radar receiver is made with similar dipoles and connected to an amplifier which converts the signal to an audio signal. In this experiment, two receivers are connected in parallel by a "T" in the line. As the relative distance of the two receivers is changed, one hears maxima and minima on the receiver depending on the number of wavelengths separating the receivers.

O1-2. SINGLE SLIT DIFFRACTION-RADAR

A plane wave is produced by connecting the wave generator of a radar set to a dipole radiator placed at the focus of a parabolic reflector. The wave is intercepted by a large metal sheet which has a single slit parallel to the dipole and of width comparable to the wavelength of the radar wave. Three centimenter radar keeps sizes down in this experiment. The receiver is now moved around on the far side of the screen and gives maxima and minima which depend on the phase relations of the waves from various parts of the open slit.

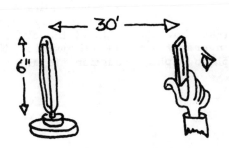

O1-3. SINGLE SLIT DIFFRACTION OF LIGHT

A long straight wire filament lamp serves as a light source. Photographic plates with a single scratch line are passed out to the students, who hold the scratch parallel to the wire while they view the lighted wire. They will see maxima and minima rather than a single slit image.

O-31

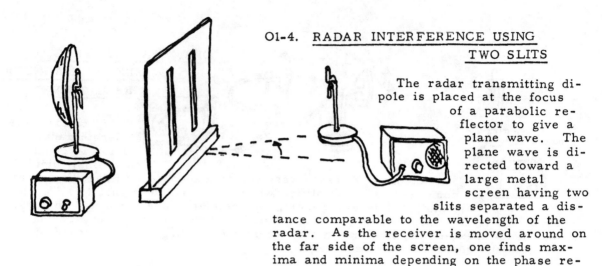

O1-4. RADAR INTERFERENCE USING
TWO SLITS

The radar transmitting dipole is placed at the focus of a parabolic reflector to give a plane wave. The plane wave is directed toward a large metal screen having two slits separated a distance comparable to the wavelength of the radar. As the receiver is moved around on the far side of the screen, one finds maxima and minima depending on the phase relations of the waves from the two slits.

O1-5. LIGHT INTERFERENCE USING TWO SLITS

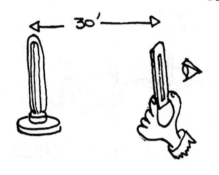

A long single filament lamp is used as a source. The student has an emulsion plate with two scratches close together and views the filament through the two scratches. He will see several maxima and minima rather than two slits.

O1-6. SINGLE SLIT DIFFRACTION
PATTERN

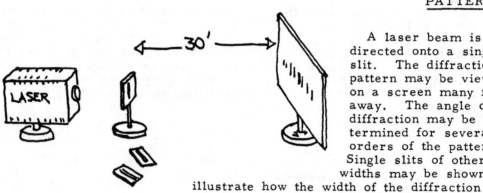

A laser beam is directed onto a single slit. The diffraction pattern may be viewed on a screen many feet away. The angle of diffraction may be determined for several orders of the pattern. Single slits of other widths may be shown to illustrate how the width of the diffraction varies inversely with the slit width. Narrow slits of known size can be made best by photographic reduction steps. One may also use a well machined adjustable slit.

O-32

O1-7. ADJUSTABLE SLIT

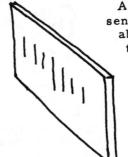

A laser beam is sent through an adjustable single slit. As the slit is made more narrow, the diffraction pattern broadens.

O1-8. PHOTODIODE RECEIVER ARRAY

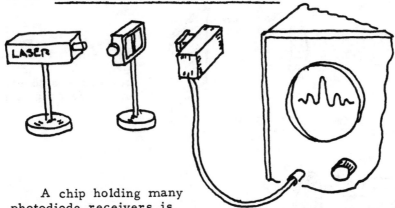

A chip holding many photodiode receivers is placed in the diffraction pattern of a slit. A rather complicated switching circuit (from Reticon) allows the photodiode array to be scanned and presented in sequence on an oscilloscope. The relative intensities of the fringes many be studied.

O1-9. INTERFERENCE PATTERN OF TWO SLITS

A laser beam is directed through a double slit and the interference pattern is observed on a screen beyond the slit. The angles for the various orders may be determined, and with a known distance between the slits the wave length of the laser light may be calculated. Double slits with different distances between them may be shown to illustrate the decrease in the distance between interference fringes as the separation of the slits increases.

O1-10. NUMBER OF SLITS

The laser is directed onto various numbers of narrow slits, but always with the same spacing between slits. As the number of slits increases, the positions of the maxima in the interference pattern remain fixed but the intensity increases more and more fringes become visible. Eventually one has the diffraction grating, with the same interference conditions as found for a double slit.

O1-11. FRESNEL BIPRISM

Laser light is sent through a Fresnel biprism. The biprism produces two interfering sources to give an interference pattern on a screen.

O1-12. BILLET HALF LENS

This is a split convex lens which behaves similar to the Fresnel biprism to produce interference on a screen.

O1-13. TWO DIMENSIONAL GRATING

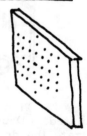

Crossed gratings are placed in a laser beam. One obtains a lattice of interference points on a distant screen.

O1-14. MODEL OF CRYSTAL LATTICE

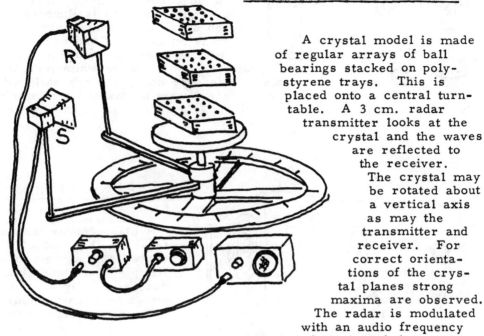

A crystal model is made
of regular arrays of ball
bearings stacked on poly-
styrene trays. This is
placed onto a central turntable. A 3 cm. radar
transmitter looks at the
crystal and the waves
are reflected to
the receiver.
The crystal may
be rotated about
a vertical axis
as may the
transmitter and
receiver. For
correct orienta-
tions of the crys-
tal planes strong
maxima are observed.
The radar is modulated
with an audio frequency
so that detection of the maxima
is accomplished by listening to the sound. (The apparatus is
made by Welch.)

O1-15. INTERFERENCE IN THIN SHEETS

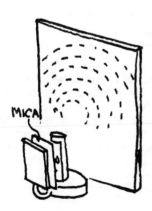

A mercury lamp, which is filtered to give
only blue light, is placed in front of a thin
mica sheet backed by a piece of black velvet.
There are reflections from the front and back
surfaces of the mica sheet which give two
images separated by twice the thickness of the
sheet. These images serve as coherent
sources and give an interference pattern by
reflection onto a screen.

O1-16.   SOAP FILM INTERFERENCE

A flat container with a black felt bottom
has a lip across which one may support a
soap film.   The film is illuminated with a
carbon arc.   Images are produced from reflections on the front and back surfaces of
the film and are put onto a screen with a
projection lens.   Since white light is used,
the interference conditions are satisfied differently for different wavelengths and the interference
fringes are colored.   The positions of the fringes change as the film evaporates.

O1-17.   NEWTON'S RINGS

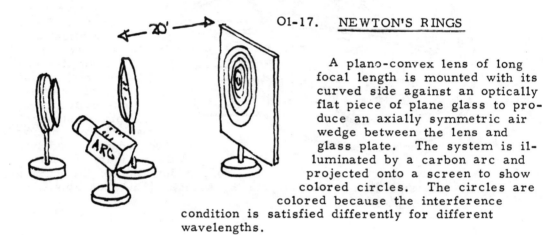

A plano-convex lens of long
focal length is mounted with its
curved side against an optically
flat piece of plane glass to produce an axially symmetric air
wedge between the lens and
glass plate.   The system is illuminated by a carbon arc and
projected onto a screen to show
colored circles.   The circles are
colored because the interference
condition is satisfied differently for different
wavelengths.

O1-18.   AIR WEDGE

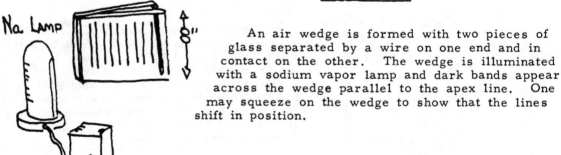

An air wedge is formed with two pieces of
glass separated by a wire on one end and in
contact on the other.   The wedge is illuminated
with a sodium vapor lamp and dark bands appear
across the wedge parallel to the apex line.   One
may squeeze on the wedge to show that the lines
shift in position.

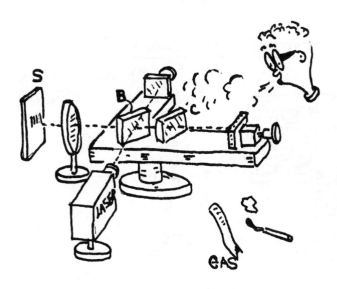

O1-19. MICHELSON INTERFEROMETER

A laser beam is directed at the beam splitter, B, which is a parallel-sided
piece of half-silvered glass that reflects part of the beam toward one adjustable
mirror and transmits the rest of the beam toward the other mirror. Both
mirrors reflect the light directly back to the front of the beam splitter, where
the beams come together and proceed toward the screen S where they produce
interference patterns. The compensator C is added so all light paths must
include three thicknesses of glass, and thus keep the optical path lengths more
equal.

Smoke is blown across the system so the students can see all the paths of
all the beams through the system. Either of the mirrors may be moved to
show the fringes shift. Illuminating gas or hot air from a burned match may
be introduced into one of the paths to show how the change in optical path length
will shift the fringes.

After good alignment is obtained with a laser, one can move one of the
mirrors a large distance and discuss coherence lengths. A helium lamp may
be substituted for the laser and the coherence length is much shorter. For
white light, the coherence length is very short and one must have the two arms
of almost exactly equal optical length.

O1-20. MICHELSON INTERFEROMETER WITH RADAR

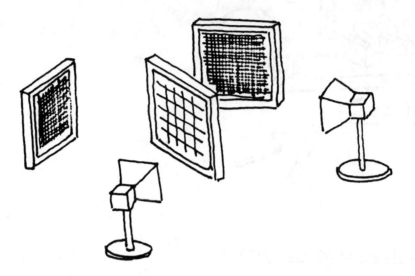

     Three squares of screen are made. Two of the squares
are made of fine window screen to act as plane wave reflectors.
The third screen has a chicken wire mesh and serves as a half
silvered mirror. The screens are arranged in the Michelson
interferometer geometry. A 3 centimeter, audio modulated,
radar transmitter and receiver produces and detects the radar
waves that take the place of light. Maxima and minima are
heard as one moves the mirrors.

O1-21. DIFFRACTION

     A frame is constructed which holds a razor blade, some small ball bearings
at the ends of wires, and some fine wires. The edges of the objects, or the
whole objects when they are small, are placed in the path of a laser beam and
viewed on a ground glass screen. The diffraction patterns may be viewed by a
large class with the aid of television.

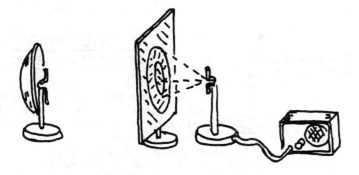

O1-22. FRESNEL ZONES

A radar transmitter is mounted at the focus of a parabolic reflector which will give a plane wave. The wave is directed at a large metal sheet which has removeable sections in the forms of concentric circular sections. The radar receiver is placed behind the metal screen at a distance such that the distance plus one-half wavelength of the radar will give the locus of the periphery of the first central removable circle. The second circle for a removable section is cut so the distance plus a full wavelength gives the locus of its periphery with the receiver as a fixed point. With the screen completely closed, there is no signal from the receiver. The central hole cover is then removed and the signal is as loud as if there were no screen present. The second ring is also removed and the received signal decreases almost to zero, even though the hole in the screen is much larger. The central cover may then be replaced and with only the ring section open, the receiver signal is again large.

O1-23. ZONE PLATE LENS

A zone plate is made by making a photographic slide of a larger correctly drawn zone plate pattern. The focal point of the zone plate can be tested with an expanded (negative lens followed by a positive lens to expand the beam) laser beam.

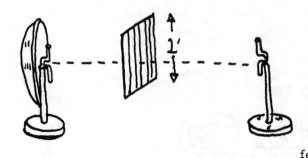

Om-1. POLARIZATION OF ELECTROMAGNETIC WAVES

A radar transmitting dipole is placed at the focus of a parabolic reflector and produces a plane wave directed at a detector several feet away. A wire grid is made of parallel wires running in only one direction. If the grid is placed between the transmitter and receiver with the wires parallel to the dipole antannae, there will be no signal to the receiver because the wires "short out" the electric field vector of the wave. If the wires of the grid are at right angles to the dipole axes and to the axis of the system, the signal is transmitted through the grid with very little attenuation.

Om-2. POLARIZATION OF LIGHT BY REFLECTION

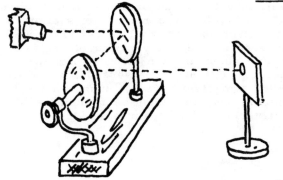

Two "black mirrors" (reflection from front face only) are mounted so light may be reflected twice. Light enters the first mirror at Brewsters angle for glass ($i + r = 90^0$) and becomes plane polarized with the electric vector along the diameter of the mirror which is normal to the incident ray. If the second mirror is oriented the same way, it can again reflect the light to a screen. If the second mirror is oriented by rotating it so it has no diameter normal to the first reflected ray, the second reflection becomes much weaker and eventually becomes extinct.

Om-3. CRYSTAL MODELS

A flexible model of a crystal lattice is shown with various distortions to show how the index of refraction may be different in different directions in the crystal.

Om-4. OPTIC AXIS AND INDEX ELLIPSOIDS

Wire models are constructed to show wave fronts of light in a crystal for cases where the velocity of propagation of light is different in different directions for the extraordinary ray. Consequently, the ordinary ray has a spherical wavefront and the extraordinary ray has an elliptical wavefront. The ordinary and extraordinary rays have the same velocity in the direction of the optic axis, so the spherical and elliptical wavefronts will be tangent in that direction.

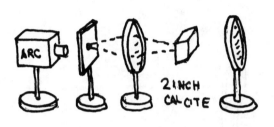 

Om-5. ORDINARY AND EXTRAORDINARY RAY

A carbon arc illuminates a small hole which is focused onto a face of a calcite crystal. The light emerges from the calcite crystal and is focused by a second lens onto a screen. There will be two focused spots, one for the ordinary ray and one for the extraordinary ray. If the crystal is now rotated about the axis of the system, the extraordinary beam will rotate while the ordinary beam remains fixed.

Om-6. POLARIZATION OF ORDINARY AND EXTRAORDINARY RAY

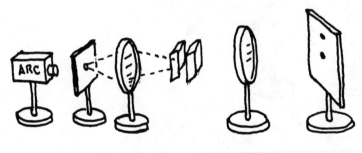

The experimental arrangement is the same as in Om-5 except that two calcite crystals are used. With both crystals oriented the same way, the crystals act in series and there is an ordinary and extraordinary ray as before. The second crystal is now rotated 45° and there will be four spots showing how each ordinary and extraordinary ray of the first crystal are resolved into an ordinary and extraordinary ray in the second crystal. At 90° rotation there will be two spots showing that the ordinary and extraordinary rays have changed their roles in the two crystals. There are again four spots for a 135° rotation. At 180° there is one spot as the second crystal refracts the extraordinary ray back to the position of the ordinary ray, thus undoing the refraction of the first crystal.

Om-7. NICOL PRISM

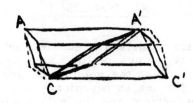

A model may be constructed to show how to cut and grind a calcite crystal and illustrate its conversion to a Nicol prism. The ends are ground off so that the oblique line makes an angle of 68° with the bottom face rather than 71°. The crystal is next cut obliquely so the cut face is normal to both the new end faces and the diagonal plane ACC'A'. In calcite the index of refraction of the ordinary ray is 1.658 while the index of refraction of the extraordinary ray is 1.49. The two parts of the Nicol prism are cemented together with Canada Balsam, which has an index of refraction of 1.530. The ordinary ray is lost by total reflection at the calcite-Canada Balsam interface.

Om-8. NICOL PRISMS AS POLARIZER AND ANALYZER

A carbon arc directs a beam of light through a pair of mounted Nicol prisms. If the optical planes of the two are oriented the same direction, light gets through the system. If the analyzer is rotated 90°, the beam does not get through the second analyzer prism.

Om-9. POLAROID AS POLARIZER AND ANALYZER

Polaroid sheet eliminates one ray by absorbtion. One sheet of polaroid may serve as a polarizer and the second may serve as the analyzer.

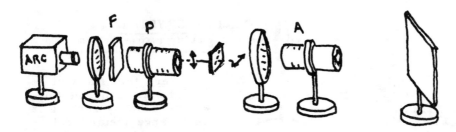

Om-10. HALF-WAVE PLATE

Light from a carbon arc is collimated and made approximately monochromatic with a filter. The light is passed through a polarizer and then through a half-wave plate. The half-wave plate is made of birefringent material and has its optic axis at 45° to the polarized beam. It is of such thickness that the relative phase change of the ordinary and extraordinary rays due to the different indices of refraction is 180°. Mounting the half-wave plate at 45° assures the presence of both components of the beam in the half-wave plate. The 180° phase shift will make the component of one beam relative to the other change sign. The light emerges polarized at 90° with respect to the incident beam, and the analyzer must be rotated 90° to obtain transmission.

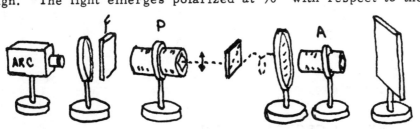

Om-11. QUARTER-WAVE PLATE

The arrangement is the same as in Om-10 except that a quarter-wave plate is used instead of a half-wave plate. The quarter-wave plate is birefringent and of such thickness that the relative change of phase between the ordinary and extraordinary rays upon going through it is 90°. The optic axis of the plate is again oriented at 45° with respect to the incident polarization in order to form both components. The 90° phase shift makes one component a maximum when the other is zero, so the emerging light must spiral to give circularly polarized light. No setting of the analyzer will now give extinction.

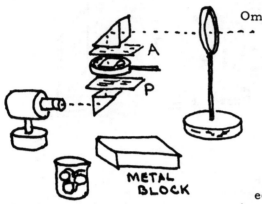

Om-12. CRYSTAL STRUCTURE IN ICE

Very thin slabs of ice are made by melting an ice cube by rubbing it on a large metal block. The thin slabs are then placed in the path of a beam of polarized light obtained using the piece of polaroid, P, on a refrigerated holder. The ice slabs are viewed through a second piece of polaroid acting as an analyzer (polaroid A). Individual ice crystals show as different colored regions. It is most interesting to look at the rings of hailstones in this manner and see the different freezing patterns.

Om-13. CRYSTAL GROWTH IN A FILM

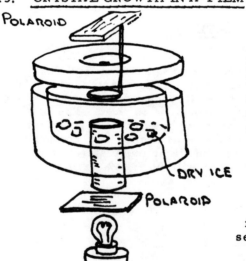

A brass tube extends into a styrofoam cavity holding dry ice. A bright light polarized with a piece of polaroid shines through the tube. A soap film on a ring is lowered through the top to make thermal contact with the tube. The soap film cools and freezes. The growth of crystals in the film during freezing is shown if the film is viewed through a second piece of polaroid.

Om-14. CHANGING COLORED DESIGNS WITH POLARIZED LIGHT

The arrangement for the half-wave plate Om-10 is used without the filter. The half-wave plate is replaced by mosaics of mica sheet oriented in different ways to form picture patterns. The varying thicknesses and varying orientations satisfy the half-wave plate condition for different wavelengths differently, so some colors get through the system and others do not. When the analyzer is rotated, the colors change to complementary colors.

TRANSPARENT TAPE

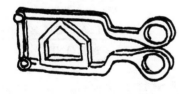

Om-15. POLARIZATION WITH A SLIDE
PROJECTOR

A slide projector is constructed so the slide holder will cary a sheet of polaroid as a polarizer and a second sheet as an analyzer, one on each side of the slide holder. A slide may be made by placing transparent tape on glass. When the slide is projected, it will show many colors according to how the half-wave plate condition is satisfied. The transparent tape has become doubly refracting during the stress of stretching while sticking it to the glass. Plastic materials under stress become doubly refracting, so models of structures may be made from transparent plastic and stressed while they are in the projector slide holder. The points of greatest strain are easily seen as can the shifting of strains due to various types of loading.

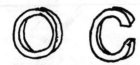

Om-15. POLARIZATION BY KARO SYRUP

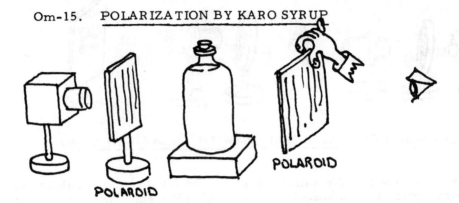

POLAROID   POLAROID

A bright source of light is polarized by a piece of Polaroid and directed through a cylindrical bottle of Karo Syrup. The light is viewed through a second Polaroid which may be rotated. Many beautiful colored patterns are seen. The Karo Syrup rotates the plane of polarization different amounts through the different path lengths in the bottle.

Om-17. BLACK GLASS POLARIZER-ANALYZER

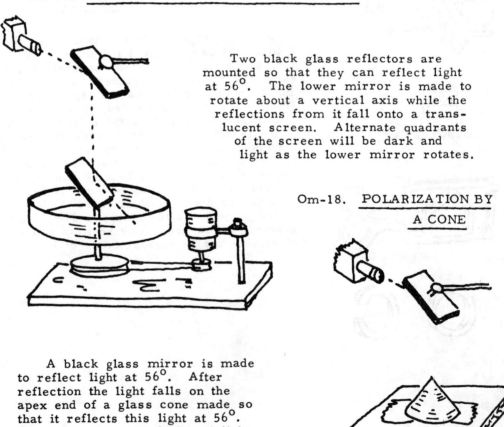

Two black glass reflectors are mounted so that they can reflect light at 56°. The lower mirror is made to rotate about a vertical axis while the reflections from it fall onto a translucent screen. Alternate quadrants of the screen will be dark and light as the lower mirror rotates.

Om-18. POLARIZATION BY
A CONE

A black glass mirror is made to reflect light at 56°. After reflection the light falls on the apex end of a glass cone made so that it reflects this light at 56°. One finds alternate dark and light areas in four quadrants around the base.

O-46

Om-19. CIRCULARLY POLARIZED RADIATION

KARO SYRUP

A clear plastic box is made with a prism resting on the inside bottom. The box is filled with Karo syrup, which can rotate the plane of polarization of the light. A piece of polaroid is at the bottom and a crossed polaroid is placed over the top. When light is shined upward through the box, many interesting colors are observed due to the different amounts of rotation by various optical path lengths in the syrup.

On-1. LIGHT SCATTERING

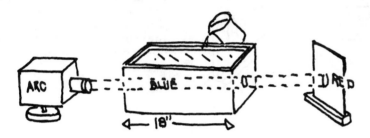

A glass tank such as an aquarium is filled with water to which about 700 ml of saturated sodium thiosulfate solution has been added. (The water and solution remain clear.) A carbon arc is directed through the tank to a screen to show a beam of white light. A beaker of dilute hydrochloric acid is then added. After a short time the water-sodium thiosulfate solution begins to get cloudy. The light scattered from the beam going through the tank appears to be blue, while the transmitted light to the screen becomes red. The blue light is scattered more than the red light.

On-2. POLARIZATION OF SCATTERED LIGHT

While doing experiment On-1, a piece of polaroid is added at A and rotated. When the polarization is vertical, the blue beam through the tank is visible when it is viewed from the side, but it is not visible if it is viewed from the top. If the polarization at A is horizontal, the blue beam can be seen from the top, but not from the side. If the polarizer A is now removed and held as indicated by B, one can not see the scattered blue light from the beam. If the polaroid is held as at C, the scattered light is visible.

Oo-1. RESONANCE RADIATION

A two liter glass bulb is evacuated and
sealed with a few iodine crystals in the bulb.
The bulb is illuminated with white light from a
carbon arc lamp. The path of the beam can be
seen through the bulb because the iodine vapor
absorbs and reradiates a characteristic wavelength.

Oo-2. MERCURY VAPOR SHADOW

A mercury lamp casts
a shadow of mercury vapor
onto a willemite screen.
One can easily see the
mercury vapor from an
open dish containing
mercury.

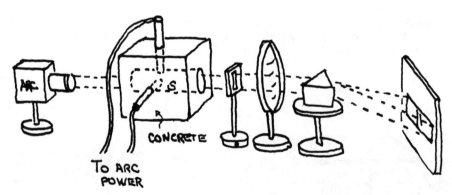

Oo-3. DARK LINE SPECTRUM

A concrete block is fitted with carbon rods so an arc can be formed in the
path of light from another carbon arc. Some asbestos soaked with salt water
made from table salt is placed in the cement block opening. The sodium is
vaporized by the arc is the cement block. The sodium vapor absorbs the characteristic "D" lines from the beam of white light from the first carbon arc.
Consequently the "D" lines will be dark in a spectrum formed with the light
emerging from the cement block.

Oo-4. ABSORBTION LINES OF SODIUM

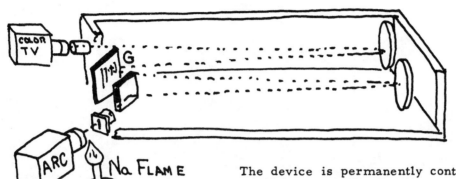

The device is permanently contained
in a rigid box to maintain alignment
(designed by B. Eaton, U. of Minn.).
Light from an arc lamp is reflected twice
to a reflection grating "G". From this grating
the light goes to another mirror and the out of the box to a
color television camera looking at the yellow region of the spectrum. A sodium flame is then introduced into the light path and
the two well resolved dark absorbtion lines of sodium appear.

Op-1. SCHLIEREN IMAGE

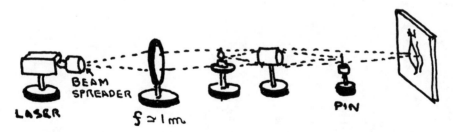

The beam of a laser is made divergent to a long focal length
lens to give a wide parallel beam. A second projection lens
focuses the laser beam onto a pin point to stop it. A gas jet or
a candlé is placed in the parallel beam at the object point of the
second lens. Both the image of the candle from its own light
and the Schlieren image in red light are seen on the screen.

MODERN
PHYSICS

(CHAIN REACTION)

MPa-1. MOUSETRAP CHAIN REACTION

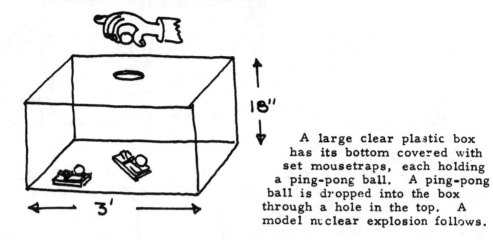

A large clear plastic box
has its bottom covered with
set mousetraps, each holding
a ping-pong ball. A ping-pong
ball is dropped into the box
through a hole in the top. A
model nuclear explosion follows.

MPa-2. GEIGER COUNTER

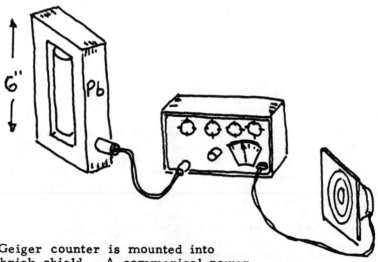

A Geiger counter is mounted into
a lead brick shield. A commerical power
supply and scaler shows the counting rate. The
output of the scaler is also connected to a loudspeaker.

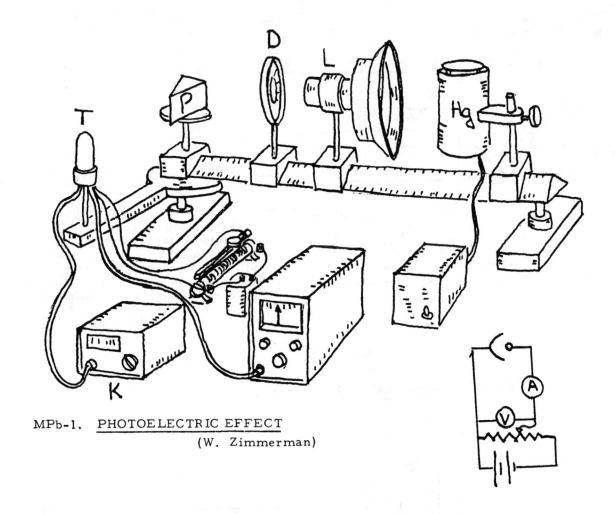

MPb-1. PHOTOELECTRIC EFFECT
(W. Zimmerman)

This experiment shows the magnitude of the photoelectric effect and allows
one to measure the energies of photons. The mercury light source, Hg, has
a slit over its exit so that one can form a line spectrum with the prism P.
The lens, L, focuses the lines on the phototube, T. The diaphragm D allows
one to vary the intensity. The voltage to the photomultiplier is furnished by a
battery and measured with the Keithley 160 Digital Voltmeter, K. The current
is measured with a HP4254 ammeter, A, although it is usually used as a null
instrument. One then measures the voltage for zero current as different lines
of the mercury spectrum illuminate the tube. For good results, one should
first have zero volts on the phototube and then find what setting of the
diaphragm will give about the same photocurrent for each line of the spectrum.

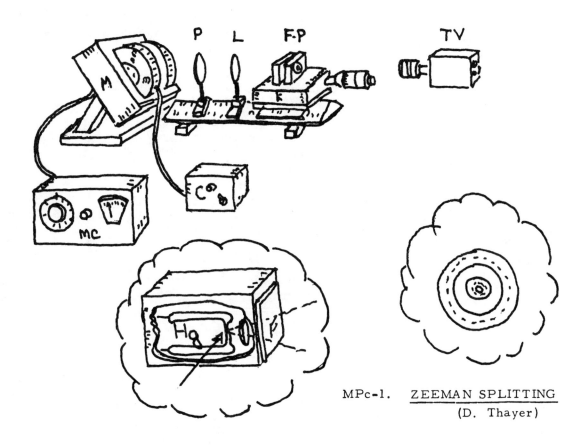

MPc-1.   ZEEMAN SPLITTING
(D. Thayer)

　　　　This experiment shows the splitting of the 5460Å green line of mercury in
a magnetic field.   The light source (shown separately) is placed between the poles
of the magnet M, which is quite large and is capable of producing a magnetic
field of about 10^4 gauss with an 8 ampere current.   The current to the magnet
is furnished by the magnet control MC.   The light source is a Cenco mercury
arc powered by the ballast conctrol C.   An applied voltage of about 5000 volts is
necessary to start the arc, but the voltage across the arc drops to the continuous
discharge voltage once the arc is going.   The light beam, which is diverging
when it emerges from between the magnet poles, first passes through an interference filter F which selects the green line.   Next the beam passes through a
polarizer P which selects the component of the light with its electric vector normal to the field of the magnet.   The rays of the diverging beam are then render-
ed parallel by the lens L and fall of the plates of a Fabry-Perot interferometer.
The final image is viewed with a TV camera.   One sees a set of concentric
green and black rings on the back side of the interferometer when the magnet is
off.   When the magnet is turned on, each of the green rings forms a black
concentric ring that divides it into two rings.